PRACTICAL OPTO-ELECTRONIC
PROJECTS

Other Titles of Interest

PRACTICAL OPTO-ELECTRONIC PROJECTS

by

R. A. PENFOLD

BERNARD BABANI (publishing) LTD
THE GRAMPIANS
SHEPHERDS BUSH ROAD
LONDON W6 7NF
ENGLAND

Please Note

Although every care has been taken with the production of this book to ensure that any projects, designs, modifications and/or programs, etc., contained herewith, operate in a correct and safe manner and also that any components specified are normally available in Great Britain, the Publishers do not accept responsibility in any way for the failure, including fault in design, of any project, design, modification or program to work correctly, or to cause damage to any other equipment that it may be connected to or used in conjunction with, or in respect of any other damage or injury that may be so caused, nor do the Publishers accept responsibility in any way for the failure to obtain specified components.

Notice is also given that if equipment that is still under warranty is modified in any way or used or connected with home-built equipment then that warranty may be void.

British Library Cataloguing in Publication Data
Penfold, R. A.
    Practical Opto Electronic Projects
    I. Title
    621.381045

    ISBN 0 85934 349 9

Printed and Bound in Great Britain by Cox & Wyman Ltd, Reading

Preface

When I first became interested in electronics in the 1960s there was a relatively limited range of opto-electronic devices available to amateur users. There were cadmium sulphide photo-resistors, one or two phototransistors, but apart from a few other devices such as cathode ray tubes and "magic-eye" tuning indicators that was about it. Things have changed quite radically over the years, and there has been a procession of new opto-electronic devices since the early 1970s. The new additions include components such as light emitting diodes (LEDs), liquid crystal displays (LCDs), fibre-optic cables and associated devices, and light sensors of various types.

Opto-electronics represents one of the most fascinating aspects of modern electronics, and many opto-electric devices are worth trying purely for their interest value. On the other hand, they mostly have as much practical application as play value, and are not just examples of the common phenomenon of clever technology in search of practical applications.

This book provides practical designs which utilize a wide variety of opto-electric devices, ranging from old technology cadmium sulphide cells and torch bulbs, to modern high power infra-red emitters, fibre-optic devices, and pyro sensors. While many of these designs are not in the "dead simple" category, they should be within the capabilities of anyone who has a certain amount of experience at electronic project construction. A few of the more simple designs are suitable for absolute beginners.

R. A. Penfold

Contents

Chapter 1

INFRA-RED DETECTORS

A surprisingly high percentage of the opto devices in electronic component catalogues are designed to operate at infra-red wavelengths, not in the visible light spectrum. One possible reason for this is simply that many types of sensor have a response which naturally peaks in the infra-red region. This is not true of all infra-red sensors though, and some of these components are "specials" that are specifically designed for operation at infra-red wavelengths. Whether they operate with infra-red "light" by accident or design, these devices are very useful, and the invisibility of infra-red "light" is crucial in some applications.

What Do We Mean by "Light"?

A detailed discussion on the nature of light would be out of place here, but it could be useful for readers to have at least a basic understanding of the subject. Fundamentally, light is a form of electromagnetic radiant energy, rather like radio waves, but at shorter wavelengths than even the shortest wavelength microwaves. This can be seen from Figure 1.1(b), which shows the full spectrum of electromagnetic waves. The scale gives the wavelengths in metres incidentally. The eye perceives the various frequencies in the visible light spectrum as a range of colours, as shown in Figure 1.1(a). In this case the scale shows the wavelengths in nanometres.

In general, the word "light" is only used to describe the part of the electromagnetic spectrum to which the human eye is sensitive. In the field of opto-electronics it is generally taken to include both infra-red and ultra-violet radiation as well. Projects which transmit and detect infra-red are included in this book, but none of the designs involve the transmission or detection of ultra-violet radiation. Until recently there were no ultra-violet components available to amateur users, apart from fluorescent tubes. It is now possible to obtain components that operate in the ultra-violet part of the spectrum, but these are expensive, and highly specialised in

1

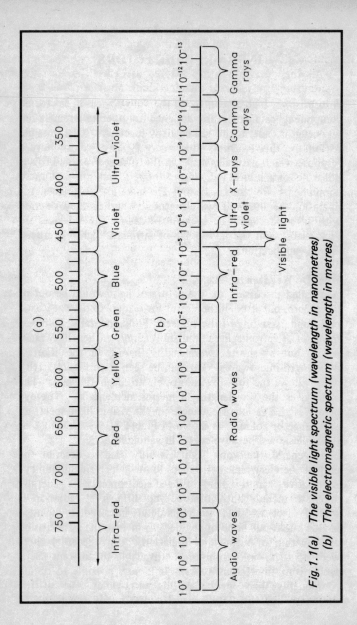

Fig. 1.1(a) The visible light spectrum (wavelength in nanometres)
(b) The electromagnetic spectrum (wavelength in metres)

nature. As there are dangers associated with ultra-violet radiation, these are not really the type of thing for experimenters to "play" with.

All the circuits in this chapter use either an infra-red transmitter or a detector of some kind. Most infra-red transmitters and detectors operate at frequencies just below the lowest visible red frequencies. All normal semcionductor infra-red devices fall into this category, and have typical peak response wavelengths of around 900 to 950nm. Devices of this type are used in some of the projects in this chapter, and they are also used in several of the projects described in Chapters 2 and 3. A passive infra-red detector project is featured in this chapter, and it operates at longer wavelengths of around 1 to 20µm. These wavelengths are well away from the visible light spectrum, and this device is really a heat detector. It is actually designed to detect the presence of people by detecting their body heat. It is based on a ceramic detector, not a semiconductor type.

Broken Beam Detector

The most simple form of broken beam detector consists of an ordinary torch bulb plus a reflector or lens to provide a fairly narrow beam of light. The beam of light is shone onto some form of photo-cell, which can be something as basic as a cadmium sulphide photo-resistor. When the beam of light is broken, usually by someone passing through it, the photocell receives a much lower light level, and its resistance increases. This is detected by a simple circuit which activates a relay. The relay in turn activates an alarm (or whatever).

This type of broken beam detector is very simple, but it has the disadvantage that it can be blocked by high ambient light levels. Also, the beam of light is easily detected, which is obviously a major drawback in security applications. This is one of the main applications of a broken beam detector. A system based on a modulated infra-red beam is better suited to most practical applications. The broken beam detector featured here uses a modulated infra-red beam, and Figure 1.2 shows the basic arrangement used.

The transmitter is very simple, and is little more than an audio oscillator operating at a frequency of a few kilohertz.

3

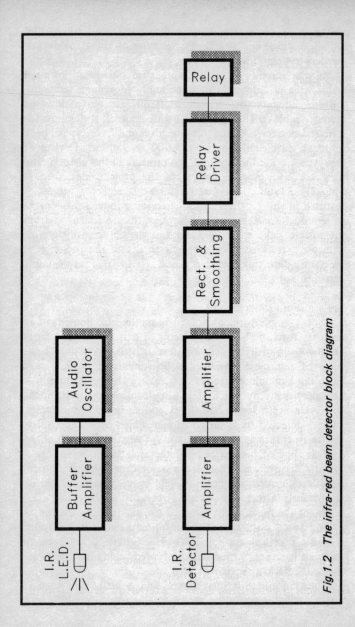

Fig.1.2   The infra-red beam detector block diagram

The exact operating frequency of the oscillator is not particularly important, but it needs to be fairly high so that the receiver can easily distinguish between the pulse signal and any background noise. In particular, it needs to be able to readily detect the pulse signal while ignoring any 100Hz "hum" from mains powered lighting. On the other hand, the frequency must not be set so high that the LED and detector operate inefficiently. A frequency of a few kilohertz offers a good compromise.

The oscillator drives an infra-red LED via a buffer amplifier. The latter enables the LED to be driven at a high current, but the signal from the LED is still fairly weak. It is for this reason that a modulated beam is used. A modulated beam can be detected against an infra-red background level that would completely swamp a d.c. system. The system is largely immune to problems from high but stable levels of background infra-red. In theory the system could be blocked by a strong background infra-red level that saturated the detector, but in reality there is little risk of this occurring. Using a modulated beam also avoids the problems with drift that inevitably arise with a highly sensitive d.c. system.

At the receiver an infra-red detector diode converts the pulses of infra-red radiation into minute electrical pulses. These are amplified by a two-stage high gain amplifier. The pulses from the detector may be under one millivolt peak-to-peak, but the total voltage gain through the amplifiers is well over 80dB. This gives a signal level of a few volts peak-to-peak to the next stage, which is a simple rectifier and smoothing circuit. This produces a strong d.c. output signal to the final stage, which is a relay driver. The relay is normally held in the "off" state, but it is turned on if the d.c. level from rectifier and smoothing circuit drops to a low level. Of course, this is exactly what happens if the infra-red beam is blocked. The signal fed to the rectifier and smoothing circuit then only consists of background "hiss", and this is at too low a level to hold the relay driver in the "off" state. The system therefore provides the required broken beam detection.

The range of the basic system is quite short, and is typically about one to two metres, depending on the particular types of LED and photodiode used. This is sufficient for some applications, such as where the beam merely has to traverse a doorway or corridor. In many applications a much greater range will be required, and this can be accomplished by adding a simple optical system. All that is needed is one or two inexpensive lenses, and a maximum operating range of 10 metres or more should then be possible. This is a more practical approach to obtaining greater range than using a higher transmitter power and a hyper-sensitive receiver. An optical system is likely to be much cheaper, provide a greater operating range, and give much better reliability.

Transmitter

The circuit diagram for the transmitter appears in Figure 1.3. This is basically just a 555 timer used in the standard astable (oscillator) mode. It provides a roughly squarewave output signal at pin 3. The operating frequency is set at approximately 4.5kHz by timing components R1, R2, and C2. TR1 is the buffer amplifier, and this is a straightforward emitter follower stage. It drives the infra-red LED (D1) via current limiting resistor R3. The 555 can actually provide quite high output currents, but using an external buffer stage enables the LED current to be set more accurately. The LED current is about 100 milliamps, but as the LED is switched off for about 50 percent of the time the average LED current is approximately 50 milliamps. This is the maximum average current rating for most 5 millimetre diameter infra-red LEDs. The current consumption of the entire circuit is slightly higher, at around 56 milliamps.

A TIL38 is specified for D1, but this can be any 5 millimetre diameter infra-red LED. Components of this type are not always given type numbers in component catalogues. They often seem to be described simply as "5mm infra-red LEDs", or "5mm remote control infra-red LEDs". Any 5 millimetre diameter infra-red LED of the type sold for use in remote control systems should work well in this circuit. In some cases you may have a choice of wide or narrow beam LEDs. Assuming that you are not going to use a separate optical system, the narrow beam type will give a somewhat greater operating range. A wide beam LED is probably the better choice if you are going to use the transmitter with a lens.

6

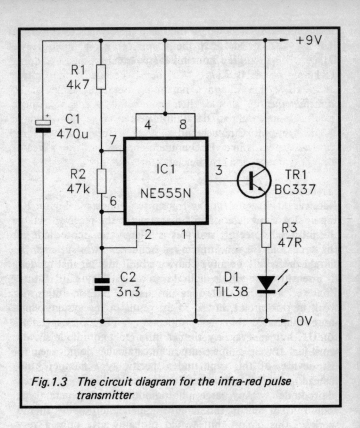

Fig.1.3   The circuit diagram for the infra-red pulse transmitter

Components for Broken IR Beam Transmitter (Fig.1.3)

Resistors (0.25 watt 5% carbon film except where noted)
R1	4k7
R2	47k
R3	47R 1 watt

Capacitors
C1	470μ 10V elect
C2	3n3 polyester

Semiconductors

IC1	NE555N
D1	TIL38 or similar (see text)
TR1	BC337

Miscellaneous

8 pin DIL IC holder
Circuit board
5mm LED holder
Wire, solder, etc.

Receiver

Figure 1.4 shows the circuit diagram for the receiver. D1 is the infra-red detector, and this is a large area photodiode of the type sold for use in infra-red remote control systems. It should preferably be a type having a built-in filter that renders it insensitive to visible light (a so-called "daylight" filter). However, a device that does not have a built-in filter will work in this circuit, but it might result in the system being more vulnerable to noise problems. A TIL100 is specified for D1, but any vaguely similar infra-red photodiode should work just as well. Some component catalogues do not seem to list devices of this type under specific type numbers, but instead simply describe them as something like an "infra-red photodiode". Any large photodiode of this general type should work well in this circuit. Small photodiodes should work in this circuit, but would probably give only a very short operating range.

The TIL100 and similar components do not have a built-in lens. This results in a very limited maximum range of about one metre. There is an alternative form of infra-red photo-diode that has a built-in lens, and looks very much like a LED. A device of this type, provided the LED and detector are aligned correctly, should offer a maximum operating range of about 2 metres. However, as pointed out previously, many practical applications will require an operating range of several metres, and will therefore need a proper optical system. A photodiode which does not have an integral lens is probably a better choice if the unit will be used with a systems of lenses.

8

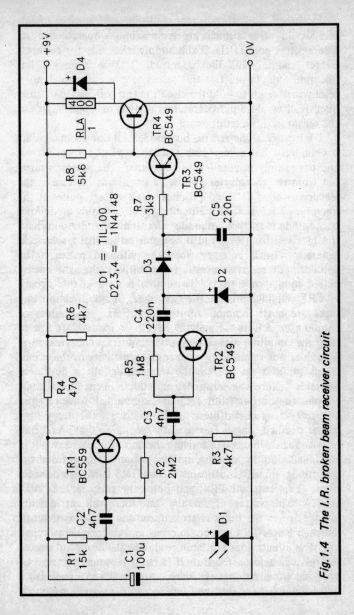

Fig.1.4 The I.R. broken beam receiver circuit

9

In theory, a phototransistor could be used in place of D1, and would offer a much greater maximum operating range. The emitter goes to the 0 volt supply, the collector connects to R1 and C2, and the base lead (if there is one) is left unconnected. In practice this seems to give a very high noise level which tends to hold the circuit in the "off" state. Consequently, I would only recommend the use of a photodiode as the sensor in this circuit.

D1 is used in the reverse bias mode. Like any semiconductor diode, it has a very high resistance when reverse biased, and passes only minute leakage currents. The pulses of infrared from the transmitter produce a significant increase in the leakage level of D1, and produce small voltage pulses at the junction of R1 and D1. The alternative operating mode for a photodiode is the voltaic mode. In this mode it does not have the bias resistor (R1), and it operates rather like a solar cell, generating small voltages from the infra-red pulses. The voltaic mode tends to give lower sensitivity than the reverse biased mode, so it is the latter that is used in this circuit.

TR1 and TR2 provide the two stages of amplification, and these are both common emitter amplifiers. The values of coupling capacitors C2 and C3 have been made quite low so that the amplifier has a very poor low frequency response. This does not significantly reduce the sensitivity of the circuit to the 4.5kHz signal from the transmitter, but it does considerably reduce the sensitivity to 100Hz mains "hum". C4 couples the output from TR2 to a simple half-wave rectifier and smoothing circuit based on D2 and D3. The decay time of the circuit is only a fraction of a second, so that even briefly breaking the beam will activate the unit.

Under standby conditions the output voltage from the smoothing circuit is sufficient to bias TR3 hard into conduction. This cuts off TR4, and holds the relay in the "off" state. The voltage from the smoothing circuit quickly subsides when the beam is broken, causing TR3 to switch off. R8 then biases TR4 into conduction, and the relay is switched on. The circuit does not latch, and once the beam is restored, the relay switches off again. If latching is required it must be provided by additional circuitry. A typical application for a unit of this type is as a sensor for a burglar alarm system. A pair of normally closed relay contacts would then be wired in series with the other sensor switches, and the main alarm system would provide entry and exit delays, latching, etc.

D4 is a protection diode which suppresses the high reverse voltage that would otherwise be generated across the relay coil as it is switched off. Semiconductors are very intolerant of high voltages, and this reverse voltage could easily damage the semiconductors in the circuit if it was not suppressed.

In some applications it is a logic compatible output that is required, rather than a set of relay contacts. The relay contacts could be made to provide a logic compatible signal, but this would be doing things the hard way. It is easier if D4 is omitted and the relay coil is replaced with a 1k resistor. This gives a CMOS compatible output, provided the CMOS circuit is used on the same supply as the receiver circuit. If a TTL compatible output is required, simply omit both the relay and D4. The collector of TR4 then provides an open collector output that can pull a TTL input low. A 2k2 pull-up resistor from the collector of TR4 to the +5 volt logic supply can be included, but satisfactory results will almost certainly be obtained without this component.

The current consumption of the circuit is typically about 2.8 milliamps under standby conditions. It is substantially higher than this when the relay switches on, and the exact current consumption depends on the resistance of the relay used. The current consumption is typically around 30 milliamps with the relay activated. I used a relay having a 6 volt 400 ohm coil, but any 6 volt relay having suitable contacts and a coil resistance of about 200 ohms or more should work well in this circuit. A 12 volt relay can be used, but in most cases this will require the supply potential to be raised to 12 volts in order to give reliable operation of the relay.

Construction of the circuit is reasonably straightforward, but bear in mind that this circuit has a substantial amount of voltage gain and a fairly wide bandwidth. Also, the input and output of the circuit are in-phase. The component layout therefore needs to be carefully designed in order to avoid problems with instability due to stray feedback. In particular, keep the wiring around D1 well away from the wiring to the collector of TR2. The wiring to D1 must either be very short,

11

or a screened cable should be used.

Components for Broken IR Beam Receiver (Fig.1.4)

Resistors (all 0.25 watt 5% carbon film)

R1	15k
R2	2M2
R3	4k7
R4	470R
R5	1M8
R6	4k7
R7	3k9
R8	5k6

Capacitors

C1	100μ 16V elect
C2	4n7 polyester
C3	4n7 polyester
C4	220n polyester
C5	220n polyester

Semiconductors

D1	TIL100 or similar (see text)
D2	1N4148
D3	1N4148
D4	1N4148
TR1	BC559
TR2	BC549
TR3	BC549
TR4	BC549

Miscellaneous

RLA1   6 volt coil, 200R or greater coil resistance
(see text)
Circuit board
Wire, solder, etc.

Optical Systems

As pointed out previously, the range of the broken infra-red beam detector can be greatly improved by adding a simple optical system. Although the basic system offers a maximum operating range of only about one to two metres, a simple optical system based on a couple of inexpensive lenses will increase this to at least 10 metres. In fact a single lens is sufficient if only a modest increase in range is needed. With one lens it should be possible to obtain a range of up to about 3 metres or so.

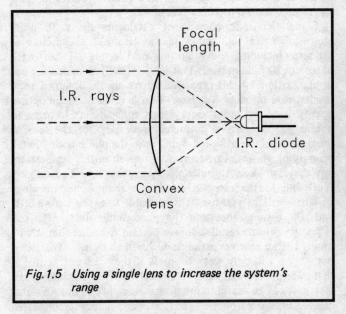

Fig.1.5 *Using a single lens to increase the system's range*

Figure 1.5 shows the way in which a single lens is used. The effect of the lens is to gather up the infra-red energy over a relatively large area, so that the amount of energy received is comparatively large. This energy is then concentrated onto the small sensitive area of the photodiode. This gives an output signal from the photodiode that is likely to be ten or more times higher than the signal obtained without the aid of a lens.

The lens must be a positive (convex) type, and in order to be reasonably effective it must have a diameter of 25 millimetres or more. The focal length is not of great importance in theory, but in practice focal lengths of more than about 150 millimetres will be awkward to use due to the large distance required between the lens and the front of the photodiode. This distance must be approximately equal to the focal length of the lens. It is not advisable to use a lens having a very short focal length, since the positioning of the photodiode might then become very critical. Probably the best choice is a lens of about 25 to 50 millimetres in diameter, having a focal length of about 50 to 100 millimetres.

Some electronic component catalogues list a 30 millimetre diameter red tinted plastic lens (37 millimetres in diameter including the mounting rim) having a focal length of about 80 millimetres. This is specifically designed for use in applications of this type, and I have always obtained good results from this low cost lens. Bear in mind that high optical quality is of no importance in this application. In order to obtain good results it is merely necessary for the lens to roughly focus the infra-red signal onto the photodiode. Small magnifying glasses also seem to work well in this application, but they are likely to be relatively expensive, and often have focal lengths that are slightly longer than would be ideal.

Whatever lens you use, it is advisable to experiment a little with the distance between the photodiode and the lens in order to optimise results. It is important to realise that adding a lens to the receiver makes it highly directional. Therefore, the system will only work properly if the receiver is aimed at the transmitter reasonably accurately. When setting up the system it can be useful to monitor the amplifier's output signal using a crystal earphone. The earphone is simply connected between the collector of TR2 and the 0 volt earth rail. The 4.5kHz signal from the transmitter is at quite a high frequency, but it is still clearly audible by anyone with normal hearing. The system can then be adjusted for the loudest signal with the lowest background noise level.

Twin Lens System
In order to obtain a maximum range of 10 metres or so it is

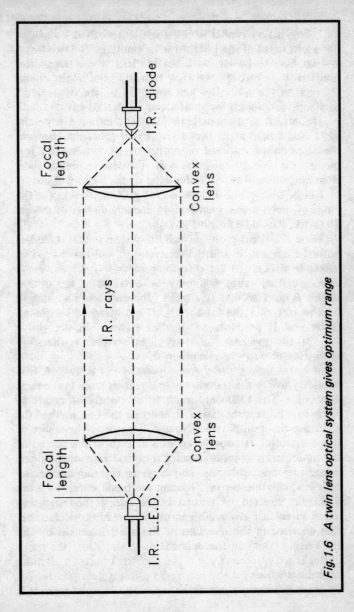

Fig. 1.6 A twin lens optical system gives optimum range

necessary to use a twin lens optical system, as shown in Figure 1.6. This is very similar to the single lens method, but it also has a lens ahead of the LED at the transmitter. The two lenses do not have to be identical, but the lens at the transmitter needs to have broadly the same characteristics as the one at the receiver (i.e. a positive lens having a diameter of about 25 to 50mm, and a focal length of about 50 to 100mm).

The effect of the lens is to focus the infra-red from the LED into a tight beam that diverges very gradually. Because the beam does not spread very much over a distance of a few metres, the intensity remains high even several metres away from the transmitter. The focusing of the beam will not be perfect of course, and the beam does gradually weaken as the range of the system is increased. A maximum range of at least 10 metres should be possible though.

There is a slight problem with this system in that it renders both the transmitter and the receiver highly directional. This makes it difficult to get everything accurately set up, but a long operating range will only be obtained if the optical system is quite accurately aligned. The situation is not helped by the fact that the infra-red LED only transmits infra-red radiation. It produces no significant output in the visible part of the spectrum, and its "light" output is therefore totally invisible to a human observer.

In order to get the system operating correctly it is first necessary to get the transmitter to direct its beam in the right direction. The LED only needs to be slightly off-centre in order to misdirect the beam. I find that the best method for adjusting the transmitter is to use the receiver as a sort of signal detector. It works best as a detector if the output of the amplifier is monitored using a crystal earphone, as described previously. If you start close to the transmitter and then gradually move away, you can determine where the beam is actually directed. A bit of trial and error is then needed in order to correct any misalignment of the LED. Remember that an error in the direction of the beam is caused by the LED being "out" in the opposite direction. Once the transmitter is set up correctly it is just a matter of using a bit more trial and error to get the receiver's optical system adjusted for optimum performance.

Twin Beam System

Although a broken infra-red beam detector is ideal for a number of applications, there is a potential flaw in a system of this type. The problem is simply that the effective beam width of the system is very narrow. If the system includes one or two lenses, the effective beam width is round 25 to 50 millimetres. If no lens system is used, other than any built-in lenses the LED and photodiode may have, the effective beam width is only a few millimetres. This can result in false alarms due to moths or other insects flying through the beam.

There are various approaches to combatting this problem, but the twin beam system is probably the most effective. The general idea is to have two transmitters and two receivers operating as what are virtually independent broken beam systems. The two beams are normally quite close together, and they would typically be about 300 to 400 millimetres apart, and one above the other. The system is arranged so that the relay is only activated if both beams are broken simultaneously. Someone passing through the beams will break both beams at the same time, and will activate the system. An insect will only break one beam, or will break both beams at separate times. Either way, an insect will fail to trigger the unit and produce a false alarm.

The original transmitter circuit (Fig.1.3) is also suitable for the dual beam version of the circuit. Of course, two of these circuits are required, one to provide each beam. The original receiver circuit (Fig.1.4) is also suitable for one section of the receiver, but the other section requires the slightly simplified circuit of Figure 1.7. This is basically the same as the original circuit, but it lacks the output stage and relay. Instead, it shares the output stage and relay of the other receiver circuit. If either TR3 in the main receiver circuit or TR7 in this circuit is switched on, TR4 in the main circuit will be held in the off state, and the relay will not be switched on. The relay will only be activated if both TR3 and TR7 are switched off. This only happens if both beams are broken simultaneously.

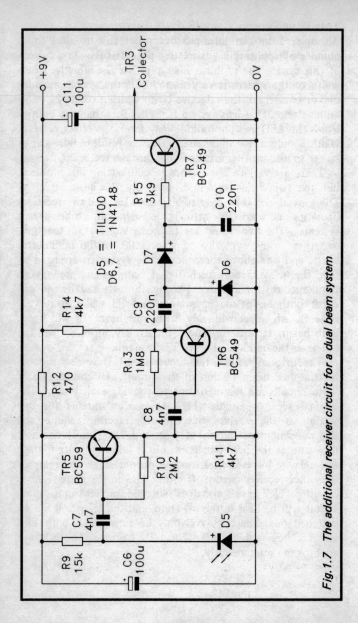

Fig.1.7 The additional receiver circuit for a dual beam system

18

Components for Dual Beam IR System Transmitter
Two sets of the components listed previously for the single
beam transmitter (Fig.1.3) are required.

Components for Dual Beam IR System Receiver
(Figs 1.4 & 1.7)

Resistors (all 0.25 watt 5% carbon film)

R1	15k
R2	2M2
R3	4k7
R4	470R
R5	1M8
R6	4k7
R7	3k9
R8	5k6
R9	15k
R10	2M2
R11	4k7
R12	470R
R13	1M8
R14	4k7
R15	3k9

Capacitors

C1	100μ 16V elect
C2	4n7 polyester
C3	4n7 polyester
C4	220n polyester
C5	220n polyester
C6	100μ 16V elect
C7	4n7 polyester
C8	4n7 polyester
C9	220n polyester
C10	220n polyester
C11	100μ 16V elect

Semiconductors

D1	TIL100 or similar (see text)
D2	1N4148

D3	1N4148
D4	1N4148
D5	TIL100 or similar
D6	1N4148
D7	1N4148
TR1	BC559
TR2	BC549
TR3	BC549
TR4	BC549
TR5	BC559
TR6	BC549
TR7	BC549

Miscellaneous

RLA	6 volt coil, 200R or greater coil resistance (see text)
	Circuit board
	Wire, solder, etc.

Broken Beam Camera Trigger

Opto-electronic camera triggers are becoming increasingly popular. At one time this sort of thing was quite difficult to set up because the cameras of the time could only be fired mechanically. In order to trigger them automatically via some form of electronic detector it was necessary to build an electromagnetic device that would provide mechanical triggering of the camera from an electrical stimulus. This tends to be more difficult than one might think, especially with the many cameras that require a fair amount of pressure on their shutter buttons before they will fire. Also, there is often a short delay between the trigger circuit being activated and the camera's shutter actually opening. This can be crucial in many applications of automatic camera triggering, where it is often fast moving subjects that must be photographed.

Technology progresses, and these days many SLR cameras have a socket for an electric shutter release. In fact some recent cameras do not accept a conventional cable release, and can only be fired via their shutter button or an electric cable release. Electric release sockets permit automatic triggering via a pair of relay contacts, and with most cameras there is only a very short delay between the contacts closing and the shutter firing. An automatic trigger plus a camera of this type enables some interesting action shots to be obtained.

The most common form of optical triggering device, and the one which is probably applicable to the widest range of uses, is the broken beam type. This can be used for such things as triggering the camera as an object passes through the beam and into a bowl of water so that water splashes can be photographed. For the advanced wildlife photographer there is the challenge of photographing butterflies, other insects, and birds in flight.

There are two basic methods of taking photographs of these types, and the easiest is to use triggering of the camera. This enables photographs to be taken using flash or, where light levels are high enough, using available light. This is obviously only possible with cameras that have a suitable remote release socket, or with cameras that are fitted with a winder that provides this facility. However, as already pointed out, many of the more recent SLR cameras fall into this category.

The second method is to take the photographs under very dark conditions, with the camera's shutter set to "B" so that it can be held open while the exposure is made. The photograph is taken by triggering an electronic flashgun. These are normally fired via a set of switch contacts which form part of the camera's shutter mechanism. Consequently there is no difficulty in firing an electronic flashgun using an electronic triggering device of some kind. The drawback of this method is that it is relatively difficult to take most types of photograph under very dark conditions, and unless the photograph is taken within a reasonably short space of time there is a risk of the film becoming fogged.

The broken infra-red beam detector described previously is perfectly satisfactory if the flash triggering method is to be used. The momentary closing of its relay contacts should be perfectly adequate to trigger any electronic flashgun reliably. This might give satisfactory results with some cameras, but practical experience suggests that very brief triggering of many cameras does not provide reliable results. Totally reliable

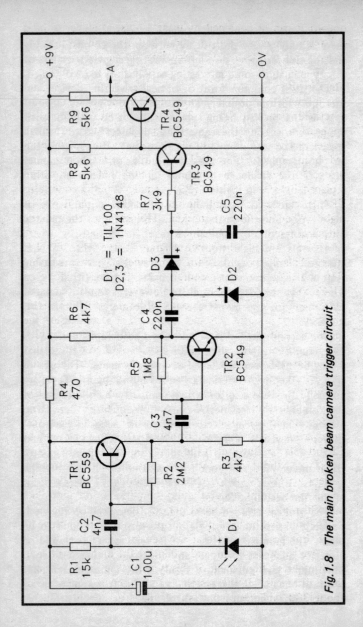

Fig.1.8 The main broken beam camera trigger circuit

22

operation can be obtained by using a pulse stretcher to hold the relay contacts closed for about half a second, so that the trigger unit mimics manual triggering via an electric release.

The Circuit

The infra-red transmitter circuit for the broken beam detector described previously (Fig.1.3) is suitable for the present application. Figure 1.8 shows the main circuit for the camera trigger receiver. This is basically the same as the broken infra-red beam detector described previously, but the relay and protection diode in the collector circuit of TR4 have been replaced by a load resistor (R9). Under standby conditions TR4 is switched off, and the output signal at point "A" is high. When the beam is broken, TR4 switches on and the output at point "A" is pulled low.

Figure 1.9 shows the circuit diagram for the pulse stretcher stage. This is just a standard 555 monostable circuit having R10 and C7 as the timing components. IC1 is triggered when TR4's collector pulses low. It then produces a positive output pulse at pin 3 of 1.1 C R seconds in duration. This gives an output pulse duration of just over half a second using the specified values for R10 and C7. This should give good results, but if necessary the pulse length can be altered quite easily. The pulse duration is proportional to the value of R10, and can therefore be changed by using a different value for this component. For example, a value of 1M5 would increase the pulse duration to about 0.75 seconds.

IC1 can directly drive the relay, which should be a 6 volt type having a coil resistance of about 200 ohms or more. A 12 volt relay can be used if the supply potential is raised to 12 volts. A pair of normally open relay contacts control the camera via SK1. The current consumption of the circuit is about 9 milliamps under standby conditions, but more like 40 milliamps during the short periods that the relay is closed.

The unit can be used with an optical system to improve its range, but bear in mind that a system of lenses gives what is effectively a wider beam, and will make the unit insensitive to small objects. Equipment of this type is often used over quite short distances. If the system is only used over a range of about 300 millimetres or less, it might be advantageous to

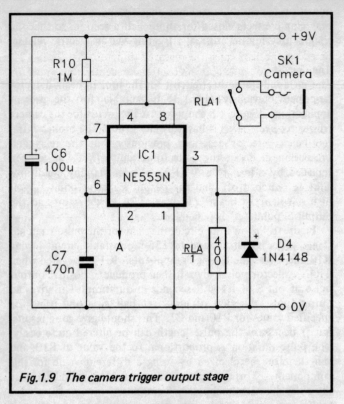

Fig.1.9 The camera trigger output stage

increase the value of R3 in the transmitter to about 150R. This will give improved sensitivity to objects that only partially block the beam. The response time of the unit is quite short, but if the fastest possible triggering is required, try making C5 a little lower in value.

Obviously the unit is only usable with a camera if you can obtain a suitable remote control lead for it. With a few exceptions, the electric release sockets on cameras are non-standard types, so there is usually no choice but to use the remote control lead produced by the camera manufacturer. A do-it-yourself lead can be used if the camera is one of the few that has a 2.5 millimetre jack socket for a "standard" remote control lead. Some manufacturers fit their remote control leads with 2.5 millimetre jack plugs at the non-camera end, but others use a different type of connector, such as 4 millimetre "banana" plugs. If necessary, the plug or plugs fitted to the lead must be removed and replaced with a 2.5 millimetre jack plug, or SK1 in the receiver unit must be replaced with a connector that will match the remote lead. If a remote lead can not be obtained, it should be possible to acquire an electric cable release. To convert this to a remote control cable simply remove the push-button switch and replace it with a 2.5 millimetre jack plug.

If the circuits are to be battery powered, in both cases six HP7 (AA) size cells in a plastic holder are suitable. The connections to the holder are made by way of a standard PP3 type battery clip. Of course, an SPST on/off switch should be added into the positive battery lead of each unit.

Components for Broken Beam Camera Trigger – Transmitter
A full set of components for the circuit of Figure 1.3 are required.

Components for Broken Beam Camera Trigger – Receiver (Figs 1.8 & 1.9)

Resistors (all 0.25 watt 5% carbon film)

R1	15k
R2	2M2
R3	4k7
R4	470R
R5	1M8
R6	4k7
R7	3k9
R8	5k6
R9	5k6
R10	1M

Capacitors

C1	100μ 16V elect
C2	4n7 polyester
C3	4n7 polyester
C4	220n polyester

C5	220n polyester
C6	100μ 16V elect
C7	470n polyester

Semiconductors

D1	TIL100 or similar (see text)
D2	1N4148
D3	1N4148
D4	1N4148
TR1	BC559
TR2	BC549
TR3	BC549
TR4	BC549
IC1	NE555N

Miscellaneous

SK1	2.5mm jack socket (see text)
RLA	6 volt coil, 200R or greater coil resistance, at least one set of normally open contacts (see text)
	Circuit board
	Remote control lead to suit camera
	Wire, solder, etc.

Reflected IR Sensors

There is an alternative to broken beam detectors in the form of reflected light detectors. Rather than detecting an object by arranging things so that it blocks light from the sensor, it is detected due to the light it reflects back to a sensor positioned next to the light source. This method is obviously dependent on the detected object being reasonably reflective. The maximum range obtained is not usually very great, even with objects that have a bright white finish. With objects of average reflectivity the range is strictly limited.

However, the range is still adequate for some practical applications, and there is clearly an advantage in a single unit system, rather than the two box broken beam method. Using a modulated beam system it is possible to detect all but the most uncooperative objects at a range of about 300 mm or so.

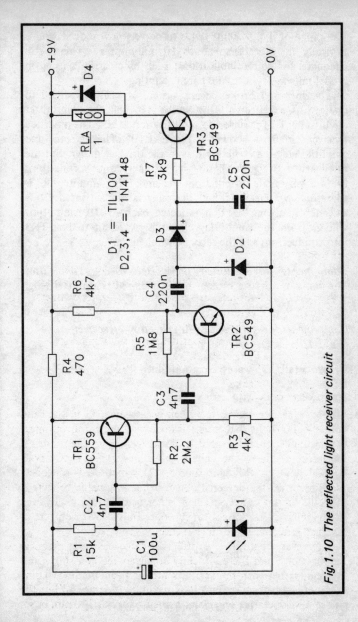

Fig. 1.10 The reflected light receiver circuit

27

The range of d.c. systems tends to be very low indeed, and is typically no more than about 20 millimetres. This is still adequate for some applications, such as position sensing in model railway layouts, and batch counting.

The infra-red broken beam system is easily modified to operate as a reflected light sensor. In fact the transmitter circuit (Fig.1.3) requires no modification at all. The modified receiver circuit is shown in Figure 1.10. The detector and amplifier stages are the same as in the original design, but the relay driver is a more basic type. Under standby conditions there is very little output from the smoothing circuit. TR3 is therefore switched off, and the relay is not activated. If a sufficiently strong signal is reflected back to D1, the output voltage from the smoothing circuit is sufficient to bias TR3 into conduction, and the relay is switched on.

Components for Reflected Light Detector – Transmitter
The same as for the broken beam infra-red transmitter (Fig. 1.3).

Components for Reflected Light Detector – Receiver
(Fig.1.10)

Resistors (all 0.25 watt 5% carbon film)
R1	15k
R2	2M2
R3	4k7
R4	470R
R5	1M8
R6	4k7
R7	3k9

Capacitors
C1	100μ 16V elect
C2	4n7 polyester
C3	4n7 polyester
C4	220n polyester
C5	220n polyester

Semiconductors
D1	TIL100 or similar (see text)

D2	1N4148
D3	1N4148
D4	1N4148
TR1	BC559
TR2	BC549
TR3	BC549

Miscellaneous

RLA   6 volt coil, 200R or greater coil resistance
(see text)
Circuit board
Wire, solder, etc.

Pulse Stripping

In practical applications there can be problems with objects
producing multiple output pulses from a reflected light sensor.
This is of no consequence if the circuit is used in an intruder
alarm, or any other application where it is simply necessary to
detect the presence of something or someone. Once the
system has been triggered, any further pulses from the detector will be of no significance. Additional pulses are a major
problem in something like a batch counting application
though. The detector may switch cleanly, providing one pulse
per object, but in practice there are often problems with
"jitter" of various types, and in a severe case each object
might be counted a hundred times or more!

If the sensor feeds into a computer, it is often possible to
use software to provide a hold-off for a second or two after
an input pulse has been detected. This prevents any spurious
pulses that may follow from boosting the count. The hardware equivalent of this is to feed the output of the detector to
a monostable multivibrator. When triggered by the sensor, this
provides an output pulse of a second or two in duration, and
effectively strips off any additional pulses from the sensor
during this period.

Figures 1.11 and 1.12 show the circuit diagram for a
reflected light sensor which includes a monostable pulse
stripper, and provides both CMOS and TTL compatible out-
puts. This is only the receiver section — the transmitter circuit

29

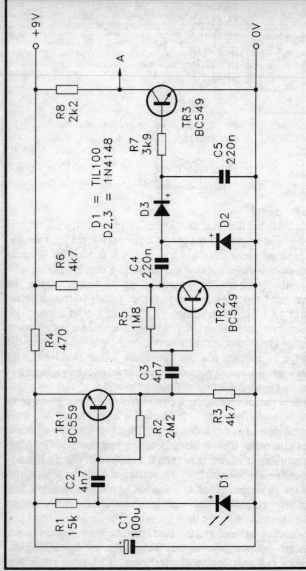

Fig. 1.11 The main circuit for the pulse stripper receiver

30

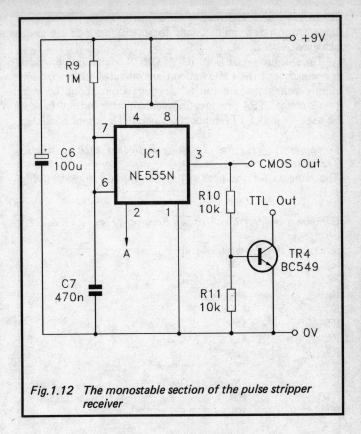

Fig.1.12 The monostable section of the pulse stripper receiver

is the same as that shown in Figure 1.3. The main receiver circuit is much the same as the original, but the relay coil and protection diode have been replaced with load resistor R8. The monostable uses a 555 in the standard configuration. The output pulse duration is about half a second with the specified values, but this must be changed to suit the particular set up in which the unit is used. The pulse duration must be long enough to ensure that there are no problems with multiple output pulses, but short enough to ensure that nothing can slip past without being detected. The output pulse duration is equal to 1.1 C R seconds (with the value of

R9 in megohms, and that of C7 in microfarads). Pulse durations from a few milliseconds to several seconds are easily achieved.

The output signal from IC1 is CMOS compatible provided the sensor and the CMOS circuit are operated from the same supply voltage (which can be anything from about 7.5 volts to 12 volts). TR4 provides an open collector output that can be used to pull a TTL input low when IC1's output goes high.

Components for Pulse Stripping Reflected Light Sensor – Transmitter
The same as for the broken beam infra-red transmitter (Fig. 1.3).

Components for Pulse Stripper Receiver (Figs. 1.11 & 1.12)

Resistors (all 0.25 watt 5% carbon film)

R1	15k
R2	2M2
R3	4k7
R4	470R
R5	1M8
R6	4k7
R7	3k9
R8	2k2
R9	1M (see text)
R10	10k
R11	10k

Capacitors

C1	100µ 16V elect
C2	4n7 polyester
C3	4n7 polyester
C4	220n polyester
C5	220n polyester
C6	100µ 16V elect
C7	470n polyester (see text)

Semiconductors

D1	TIL100 or similar (see text)

D2	1N4148
D3	1N4148
TR1	BC559
TR2	BC549
TR3	BC549
TR4	BC549
IC1	NE555N

Miscellaneous

Circuit board
Wire, solder, etc.

DC Reflected Light Sensor

There are devices intended specifically for use as d.c. (non-modulated) reflected light sensors. These are basically just a phototransistor and an infra-red LED mounted side-by-side in the same encapsulation, possibly with some form of built-in lens system as well. It is not essential to use one of these special sensors, and a separate infra-red LED and phototransistor mounted side-by-side seem to work just as well in most applications. The only proviso is that due care must be taken to avoid direct pick up of the infra-red from the LED by the phototransistor. All this requires is something like a piece of opaque plastic or card placed between the two. If you use separate components, the best choice for the phototransistor is a type that is contained in a standard LED type encapsulation, complete with a built-in lens. The infra-red LED should preferably be a type having a narrow beam.

The circuit featured here is based on the Maplin sensor type OPB706B, or the more or less identical RS/Electromail 301-606 sensor. However, it should work properly using any similar sensor, or a separate LED and phototransistor. Lead-out details for the Maplin and RS sensors are provided in Figure 1.13, which is a base view. Pin 1 is also identified by a minute "dimple" in the front surface of the encapsulation.

Figure 1.14 shows the circuit diagram for the DC reflected light sensor. The LED is fed with a current of about 30 milli-amps via current limiting resistor R1. This should be sufficient to give good results, but if necessary the LED current can be

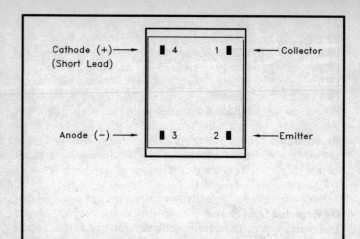

Cathode (+)
(Short Lead)

4

1

Collector

Anode (−)

3

2

Emitter

*Fig.1.13   Connection details for the OPB706B sensor
(base view)*

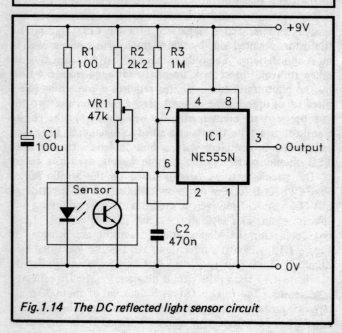

+9V

R1
100

R2
2k2

R3
1M

VR1
47k

C1
100u

7

4   8

IC1
NE555N

3   Output

6

Sensor

2   1

C2
470n

0V

Fig.1.14   The DC reflected light sensor circuit

increased to about 50 milliamps by reducing the value of R1 to 62R. R1 should not be given a lower value than this because the maximum continuous current rating of the LED (50 milliamps) would be exceeded.

The phototransistor normally has a high collector-to-emitter resistance, but this resistance falls substantially when it receives some reflected infra-red from the LED. If enough infra-red is received, the resistance of the phototransistor becomes low enough to pull pin 2 of IC1 below the trigger threshold. IC1 is then provided with an output pulse of about half a second in duration (or whatever pulse length is set by the values used for R3 and C2).

VR1 controls the sensitivity of the circuit, and the higher its resistance, the greater the sensitivity. However, this type of sensor is not immune to ambient light, even though the sensor incorporates a "daylight" filter. There seems to be a significant amount of ambient infra-red in most environments, and tungsten lighting is a prolific producer of infra-red. If VR1 is set too high in resistance the monostable will be held in the triggered state, and the circuit will cease to function. VR1 should therefore be set for the highest resistance that does not give problems with ambient light saturating the phototransistor. A little experimentation will probably be needed in order to find a setting that gives good sensitivity together with good reliability. The output of the circuit is TTL compatible, and it is also compatible with CMOS logic circuits provided they are powered from a 5 volt supply.

Components for DC Reflected Light Sensor (Fig.1.14)

Resistors (all 0.25 watt 5% carbon film)
R1	100R
R2	2k2
R3	1M

Potentiometer
VR1	47k min preset

Capacitors
C1	100μ 10V elect
C2	470n polyester

Semiconductors

Sensor	OPB706B or similar (see text)
IC1	NE555N

Miscellaneous

8 pin DIL IC holder
Circuit board
Wire, solder, etc.

Passive IR Detector

At one time passive infra-red sensors were very expensive components that were only available to professional users. These days they are available from several amateur electronics suppliers at quite reasonable prices. They are certainly one of the more interesting types of electronic sensor, and they have a number of practical applications such as burglar alarms, automatic doors, and automatic lighting.

It would perhaps be as well to start with an explanation of exactly what is meant by a "passive" infra-red detector. This is a device which detects an infra-red source of some kind, but in all common applications the source is a person. In other words it detects the body heat of someone within its field of "view", and the circuit then activates an alarm, switches on the lighting, or whatever. The infra-red systems described previously are all active systems which transmit an infra-red signal, and then detect some form of interference with this signal. A passive system does not transmit any infra-red, and relies on sufficient infra-red being provided by the objects which must be detected.

An advantage of a passive system is that it will readily detect people, because they generate large amounts of heat which makes them an easy "target". Many sources of spurious triggering, such as moths and other flying insects, do not provide sufficient heat to trigger a passive infra-red detector. Provided the system is installed and used sensibly, this gives what is usually excellent reliability with very few false alarms.

Normal semiconductor infra-red devices operate in the part of the infra-red spectrum that is close to the visible red wavelengths. In other words, at wavelengths of around 850 to

950nm. These are virtually useless for passive infra-red detection, where wavelengths of around 1 to 20μm are involved. Devices designed specifically for this application are needed in order to obtain really good results. These devices have little in common with phototransistors and photodiodes, and they are not actually semiconductors.

They are ceramic components made from a substance such as lead zirconate titanate, and they consist of a slice of the material with electrodes on opposite faces. When subjected to heating the device produces opposite electrical charges on the two electrodes. This effect is similar to the more familiar piezo electric effect which is utilized in such things as crystal microphones and ceramic pick-ups. The piezo effect generates a similar electrical signal as a result of physical distortion. Like the output from a ceramic pick-up, the output from a passive infra-red sensor, or "pyro" sensor as they are usually called, is at a high impedance.

Practical pyro sensors normally consist of more than just the sensing element, and in most cases an integral Jfet source follower buffer stage is included. Most pyro sensors have twin sensing elements. Figures 1.15(a) and (b) respectively show

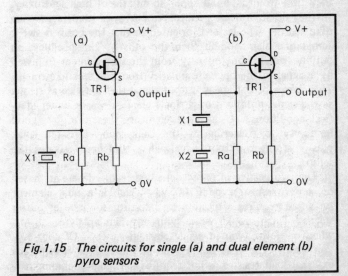

Fig.1.15   The circuits for single (a) and dual element (b)
            pyro sensors

37

the circuits for single and twin element pyro sensors. In both cases Ra is the gate bias resistor and Rb is the source load resistor. The source load resistor is not always included in the sensor, and with some sensors a discrete load resistor is therefore needed.

The twin element sensors have the two elements wired out-of-phase, which would seem to be a good way of obtaining no output signal! The background infra-red level does indeed produce zero output from the sensor, with the signal from one element cancelling out the signal from the other. This lack of response to the background signal, and to changes in the background level, is the main reason for using twin sensors. Although the sensor ignores the background infra-red signal, it will still respond properly when someone comes within the area it covers. The important point to bear in mind here is that this type of sensor is designed to detect someone moving within its field of "view", and that it is not designed to detect a stationary infra-red source.

In use a special lens or a simple grille is used in front of the sensor. This gives it zones of high and low sensitivity (Fig. 1.16). As someone moves across the sensor's field of view they pass from a "blind spot" to an area of high sensitivity. As they do so, a beam of infra-red energy is swept across the pyro sensor. The latter is oriented so that the beam is swept across one element and then the other. This produces an output signal of one polarity from the first element followed by a signal of the opposite polarity from the second element. This gives a peak-to-peak output signal that is twice as strong as the signal produced by a single element sensor under identical conditions. Using twin elements therefore gives good immunity to triggering by the background infra-red level, plus a stronger output signal when someone activates the sensor.

The two passive infra-red detectors featured here are based on a pyro sensor type E100SV1, which is a dual element type that requires a discrete load resistor for its Jfet buffer stage. They should work with any similar pyro sensors, whether of the twin or single element variety. Of course, if you use a type that has a built-in source load resistor the external load resistor is not required, although including it is

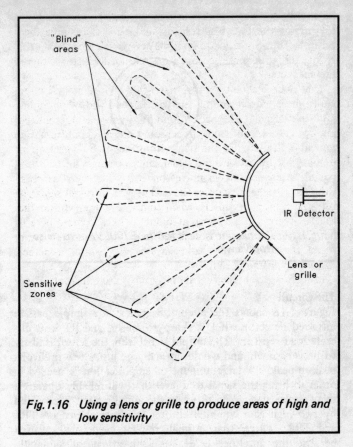

Fig.1.16 *Using a lens or grille to produce areas of high and low sensitivity*

unlikely to have a noticeable effect on performance. Connection details for the E100SV1 are provided in Figure 1.17, which is a top view. This device is housed in a metal encapsulation that is similar to the standard TO5 type used for many transistors, thyristors, etc. There is a rectangular window in the top of the case, and in use the device must be positioned so that this is horizontal. If the window is vertical, the twin elements will receive the beams of infra-red energy more or less simultaneously, and there will be little change in the output voltage from the sensor.

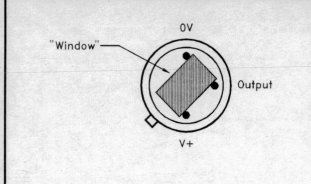

Fig.1.17 Connection details for the E100SV1 pyro sensor (top view)

Labels in figure: 0V, "Window", Output, V+

The Circuit

Figure 1.18 shows the circuit diagram for a simple passive infra-red detector. IC1 is the pyro sensor, and R1 is its discrete load resistor. The output signal from the sensor is likely to be very small, and would normally be just a few millivolts peak-to-peak. A large amount of amplification is needed in order to bring the signal to a level that will reliably operate a relay driver stage. In this case the amplification is provided by two high gain common emitter amplifiers based on TR1 and TR2. Larger than normal coupling capacitors are used because the amplifier is dealing with signals at sub-audio frequencies.

The output signal from the pyro sensor is predominantly at frequencies of around 0.5 to 2Hz. The sensing elements in the pyro device are made very thin so that they heat up reasonably rapidly when some infra-red energy is received, but the upper frequency limit is still only about 2 or 3Hz. The lower frequency limit is due to the bias resistor of the buffer amplifier leaking away the electrical charges generated by the sensing elements. Although the frequency response of the sensor is strictly limited, its response is actually well

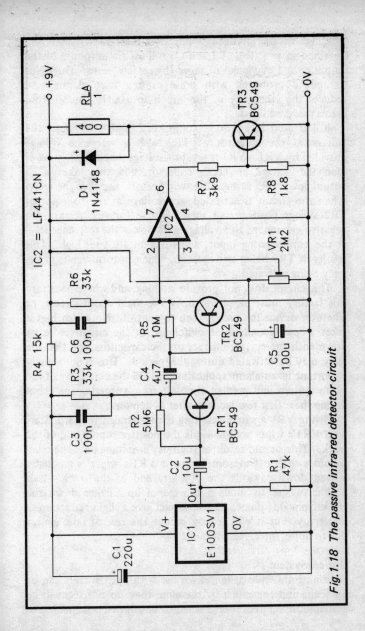

Fig. 1.18 The passive infra-red detector circuit

matched to its intended application, and good results are obtained in practice. C3 and C6 roll-off the response of the amplifier at frequencies of more than a few hertz. This helps to reduce problems with noise causing false alarms, and reduces the sensitivity of the circuit to 100Hz "hum" from mains powered lighting.

IC2 is used as a voltage comparator, and it compares the voltage at the collector of TR2 with a reference voltage provided by VR1. VR1 is set for a voltage that is slightly lower than the voltage at TR2's collector, and this takes IC2's output low. TR3 is therefore switched off, and so is the relay. When the circuit is activated, the voltage at the collector of TR2 swings positive and then negative (or vice versa). On negative excursions this voltage goes below the reference level at the non-inverting input, and IC2's output goes high. This results in TR3 being switched on, which in turn results in the relay being activated.

This circuit does not provide latching, and where necessary this facility must be provided by the main alarm circuit, or whatever device the unit is used to control. Note also that it takes a few seconds after switch-on for the circuit to settle down with the correct charges on the capacitors, and that the relay may be activated during this period. This is not usually important in an alarm application, where the exit delay of the alarm system will prevent the unit from triggering the alarm during these first few seconds after switch-on.

Giving VR1 a suitable setting is very straightforward. Start with VR1's wiper well towards the positive supply end of the track. This should result in the relay switching on. The relay should switch off at some point if VR1's wiper is gradually moved down towards the opposite end of the track. It is probably best to move the wiper a bit further down the track from this point. Doing so will give a slight reduction in sensitivity, but it will greatly reduce the risk of false alarms due to noise, drift, etc.

Optical System

Obtaining the special lenses for use with pyro sensors can be difficult, and for much of the time they do not seem to be available to amateur users. It has to be pointed out that lenses for use at visible light wavelengths, or even the shorter infrared wavelengths, are usually of no use at all with pyro sensors. Most ordinary plastic and glass lenses seem to be virtually opaque to long wavelength infra-red! If you can obtain a proper lens for use with a pyro sensor, then it should work well with this system provided it is used in accordance with the manufacturers/retailers recommendations.

Using a simple grille is the only alternative if a suitable lens can not be obtained. The E100SV1 has an angle of view of 38 degrees. A lens system can increase the effective field of view, but with a grille the coverage of the system can be no wider than the response angle of the sensor. However, for most applications a 38 degree field of coverage is adequate. A grille is easily made from a piece of plastic or aluminium. Simply cut some vertical slits in a small sheet of the material, and curve it through about 45 degrees. You may like to experiment with the sensor-to-grille distance, and with grilles having slits of various widths. My experiments would suggest that neither of these factors are particularly critical.

A grille is a simple and inexpensive solution to the problem, but this method does have one serious drawback. This is simply that a lens gives a much greater operating range. An operating range of 10 metres or more over a wide angle can be achieved using a good quality lens. Using a grille the maximum range is likely to be no more than 3 metres. Clearly this is still perfectly adequate for many applications. An advantage of the lower sensitivity provided by a grille is that the system is less prone to problems with false alarms. Using a very high level of sensitivity makes the system prone to spurious triggering due to air turbulence. Even using a grille, the unit should not be installed so that it is aimed at a radiator, or any obvious source of infra-red that could produce spurious triggering. One final point is that when handling a pyro sensor you should try to avoid touching the window. Apparently touching the window can reduce the sensitivity of the device, presumably by making the window less transparent to long wavelength infra-red energy.

Components for Passive Infra-Red Detector (Fig.1.18)

Resistors (all 0.25 watt 5% carbon film)
R1	47k
R2	5M6
R3	33k
R4	15k
R5	10M
R6	33k
R7	3k9
R8	1k8

Potentiometer
VR1	2M2 min hor preset

Capacitors
C1	220μ 16V elect
C2	10μ 25V elect
C3	100n polyester
C4	4μ7 50V elect
C5	100μ 16V elect
C6	100n polyester

Semiconductors
IC1	E100SV1 pyro sensor (or similar)
IC2	LF441CN
TR1	BC549
TR2	BC549
TR3	BC549
D1	1N4148

Miscellaneous
RLA	6 volt coil, 200R or greater coil resistance (see text)
	8 pin DIL IC holder
	Circuit board
	Wire, solder, etc.

Passive IR Alarm

This circuit is for a self-contained alarm which is based on the passive infra-red detector circuit described previously. The unit is intended to operate as a burglar deterrent for use where the cost of a comprehensive burglar alarm system is not warranted. As the unit is small and self-contained it is well suited to use in a caravan or boat. It provides a "beep-beep" alarm signal from a piezo sounder when someone walks in front of the sensor, and it has a maximum range of about 3 metres.

Figure 1.19 shows the block diagram for the passive infra-red alarm. The top row of four blocks form the basic infra-red detector, and this part of the unit is essentially the same as the passive infra-red detector described previously, but with the relay and relay driver omitted. The output of the level detector drives a latch. Even though the output of the level detector will only go high momentarily when the unit is activated, the latch will provide a continuous high output level once "set" by an output pulse from the level detector. The latch activates an LFO (low frequency oscillator), which in turn gates an audio frequency oscillator. Once the unit is activated, the LFO therefore pulses the audio oscillator on and off. This generates a "beep-beep" alarm sound from the loudspeaker (a piezo sounder) driven from the output of the audio oscillator.

There is a problem with this arrangement in that the level detector tends to produce output pulses for a few seconds after switch-on. This occurs while the coupling capacitors in the circuit take up their normal operating charges. This would make the unit trigger almost immediately at switch-on, which would clearly render it completely useless. A hold-off is needed, so that the unit can not trigger for the first few seconds after switch-on. This also gives the user a chance to switch-on the unit and get away without activating the alarm. The hold-off is provided by a monostable which automatically triggers at switch-on. It holds the latch in the "reset" state for a little under 10 seconds, which gives the amplifier stages plenty of time to settle down, and the user ample time to switch on and get well clear of the unit.

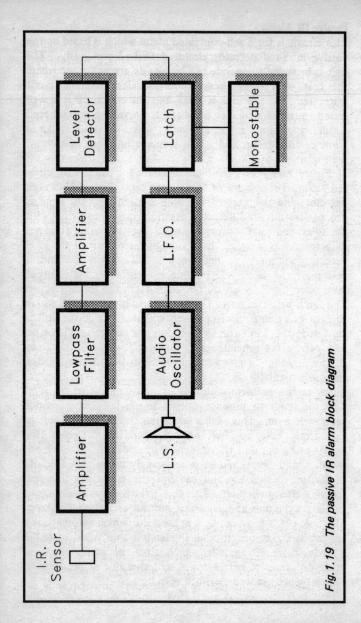

Fig. 1.19   The passive IR alarm block diagram

The unit could also be equipped with a delay circuit to prevent the alarm from sounding for a few seconds after triggering. This would give people legitimately entering the protected area time to switch off the unit before the alarm sounded. This is probably not a worthwhile feature for a small alarm of this type though, and it is almost certainly best to have the alarm sound as soon as possible when an intruder is detected. The alarm sounding for a few seconds just before the unit is switched off will presumably not disturb the neighbours.

The Circuit

The circuit for the passive infra-red alarm appears in Figures 1.20 and 1.21. Figure 1.20 shows the circuit for the detector section of the unit. This is basically the same as the passive infra-red detector described previously (Fig.1.18), and it does not warrant any further comment here.

Figure 1.21 shows the circuit for the alarm generator, latch, and monostable stages. The latch is a basic SR (set—reset) flip/flop made from two of the NOR gates in IC4. The other two gates in IC4 are not used, but their inputs are wired to the 0 volt supply rail in order to prevent spurious operations. IC3 is a low power 555 timer which is used in the monostable mode. R7 and C7 provide a trigger pulse at switch-on, and IC3's output then goes high for a time determined by R8 and C8 (about 9.5 seconds). This ensures that the latch is in the reset state once the amplifier stages have settled down to their normal operating conditions. Point "A" briefly goes high if the unit is activated, and this sets the output of the latch to the high state.

This switches on IC5, which is the low frequency oscillator. IC5 is used in the standard 555 gated astable mode, and it provides an output signal at about 2.5Hz. IC5 in turn controls another 555 gated astable, this time based on IC6 and having an output frequency of nearly 2kHz. IC6 directly drives a ceramic resonator which produces a burst of tone each time IC6 is switched on. Do not use an ordinary moving coil loudspeaker for LS1. The ceramic resonator should provide high efficiency at the relatively high operating frequency of IC6, but if desired the value of C10 can be "tweaked" to give

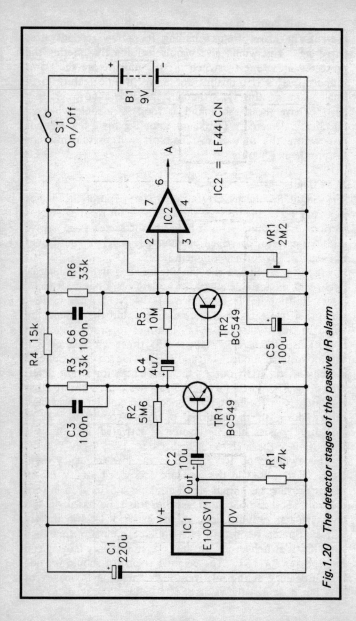

Fig. 1.20 The detector stages of the passive IR alarm

48

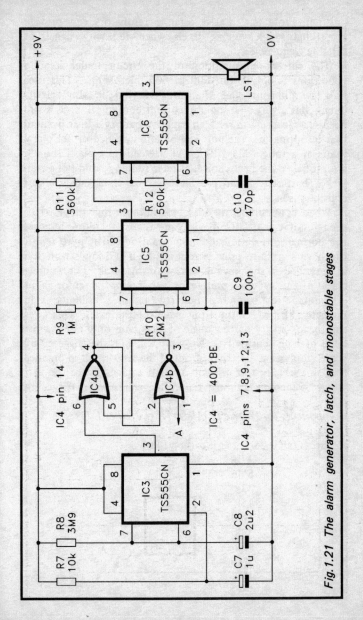

Fig.1.21 The alarm generator, latch, and monostable stages

49

optimum volume. Cased ceramic resonators can provide surprisingly high volume levels when fed with signals at suitable frequencies.

The current consumption of the circuit under standby conditions is only about 500 to 600 microamps. This rises to a few milliamps when the alarm is activated. Although the circuit has a very low standby current consumption, it is still necessary to use a fairly high capacity battery. Bear in mind that in normal use the unit will be left switched on for many hours at a time. Six HP7 (AA) size cells in a plastic holder are probably the best choice. Under standby conditions each set of batteries should provide over two thousand hours of continuous use.

When constructing the unit bear in mind that the 4001BE used for IC4 is a CMOS device, and that it therefore requires the normal anti-static handling precautions. The pyro sensor can have a grille to provide zones of high and low sensitivity, as described in the previous section of this book. For a simple alarm of this type my preference is to mount the sensor about 30 millimetres behind a hole of about 5 millimetres in diameter, drilled in the front panel of the case. This gives the sensor a very narrow angle of view, and only one narrow zone of high sensitivity. The unit will only be triggered by someone passing directly in front of the sensor, but in practice it is not usually too difficult to find a position for the unit where someone entering the room will always trigger it.

Components for Passive IR Alarm (Figs 1.20 & 1.21)

Resistors (all 0.25 watt 5% carbon film)
R1	47k
R2	5M6
R3	33k
R4	15k
R5	10M
R6	33k
R7	10k
R8	3M9
R9	1M
R10	2M2

| R11 | 560k |
| R12 | 560k |

Potentiometer

| VR1 | 2M2 min hor preset |

Capacitors

C1	220μ 16V elect
C2	10μ 25V elect
C3	100n polyester
C4	4μ7 50V elect
C5	100μ 16V elect
C6	100n polyester
C7	1μ 50V elect
C8	2μ2 50V elect
C9	100n polyester
C10	470p ceramic plate

Semiconductors

IC1	E100SV1 pyro sensor (or similar)
IC2	LF441CN
IC3	TS555CN (or similar low power 555)
IC4	4001BE
IC5	TS555CN
IC6	TS555CN
TR1	BC549
TR2	BC549

Miscellaneous

LS1	Cased ceramic resonator
S1	SPST min toggle
B1	9 volt (6 HP7 size cells in holder)
	Battery clip (PP3 type)
	Case
	8 pin DIL IC holder (4 off)
	14 pin DIL IC holder
	Circuit board
	Wire, solder, etc.

Chapter 2

PHOTOGRAPHIC PROJECTS

Electronics has played an increasingly important role in the world of photography over the last twenty years. Most of the more sophisticated cameras are now bristling with electronics, and there are numerous electronic photographic accessories available. This chapter features several simple electronic gadgets concerned with various aspects of photography.

Remote Control

An automatic trigger for a camera or flashgun is featured in the previous chapter, and it is really just a variation on the infra-red broken beam system. Rather than providing automatic triggering, the system featured here provides manual control over distances of up to 7 metres or so. It uses an infra-red link, so no connecting cables are needed between the control unit and the camera. Of course, like the automatic trigger, this system is only usable with cameras that have an electric release socket, or cameras that have this facility provided via a winder unit or motor drive.

Camera remote control systems are much used by wildlife photographers. In a typical set-up the camera is positioned close to a baited bird-table, with the focusing and other controls carefully preset to suitable settings. The photographer watches the bird-table from some distance away, and when a bird poses nicely in the right place on the bird-table, the photographer triggers the camera using some form of remote control system. Another use for a cordless remote control is to provide shake-free firing of the camera when using very long lenses or undertaking extreme close-ups. Of course, this system should also be usable in non-photographic applications that require a simple on/off remote control system for operation over short ranges.

The Circuits

The circuit diagram for the transmitter section of the camera

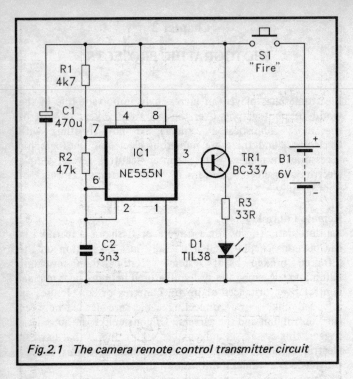

Fig.2.1 The camera remote control transmitter circuit

remote control system is provided in Figure 2.1. This is basically the same as the transmitter circuit used in several of the systems described in the previous chapter. One difference is that it is powered by a 6 volt battery supply not a 9 volt supply, which helps to keep the unit down to a more handy size. The value of R3 has been altered to maintain an average LED current of about 50 milliamps. On/off switching is provided by S1, which is a non-locking push-button switch. This effectively becomes the camera's shutter release button, and pressing S1 for about half a second fires the camera.

Figure 2.2 shows the circuit diagram for the remote control receiver. This is much the same as several of the circuits described in the previous chapter, but there are some important differences. The infra-red systems described in Chapter 1 used a fairly low level of sensitivity, but achieved good operating

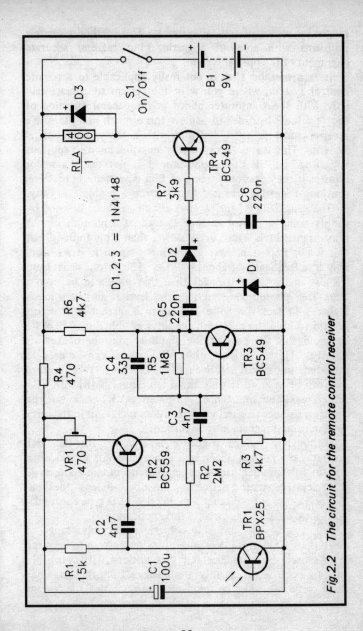

Fig.2.2   The circuit for the remote control receiver

ranges by means of optical systems. This method gives few problems with spurious triggering, but requires accurate alignment of the optical system.

It is a method that is not really applicable to a remote control system, where you want the system to operate reliably with the transmitter aimed in the general direction of the receiver. In order to achieve this a much more sensitive receiver must be used, together with a fairly basic optical system. This leaves the system more vulnerable to spurious triggering, but in this application it is not really a major disaster if the occasional frame of film is wasted. In practice, spurious triggering was not found to be a problem anyway.

The sensitivity of the receiver circuit has been boosted by simply using a phototransistor instead of a photodiode. A phototransistor is significantly slower than a photodiode, but this is not important here as the input signal is at a reasonably low frequency of about 4.5kHz. The output signal from TR1 is many times stronger than that produced by even a large area photodiode, but its noise level is also very much higher. In fact the noise level is so high that it is almost certain to hold the unit with the relay switched on. In order to avoid this the gain of the amplifier must be backed-off slightly. This is achieved using VR1, which can be used to introduce some local negative feedback to TR1. TR1's voltage gain can be reduced to only about ten times (20dB) with VR1 set at maximum resistance. In practice VR1 is set for the lowest resistance (highest gain) that does not result in the relay switching on under standby conditions.

Although a BPX25 transistor is specified for the TR1 position, any normal silicon npn phototransistor should work well in this circuit. However, in order to obtain good range it is necessary to use a device that has a built-in lens. Inexpensive phototransistors having 5 millimetre LED type encapsulations seem to work very well in this application.

The system will probably achieve a maximum range of more than 10 metres if VR1 is set just low enough to keep the relay switched off under standby conditions. It is probably best to back it off slightly from this setting though, since there could otherwise be frequent mis-fires. Also, the current consumption of the receiver would be relatively high, as there would be a fair amount of current being fed to the relay under quiescent conditions. Backing off VR1 should still permit an operating range of about 7 metres to be achieved without the aim of the transmitter being too critical. Mis-fires should then be very rare, if they occur at all.

Components for Remote Control Transmitter (Fig.2.1)

Resistors (all 0.25 watt 5% carbon film)

R1	4k7
R2	47k
R3	33R

Capacitors

C1	470µ 10V elect
C2	3n3 polyester

Semiconductors

IC1	NE555N
D1	TIL38 or similar (see text)
TR1	BC337

Miscellaneous

S1	Push to make, release to break
B1	6 volt (four HP7 size cells in plastic holder)
	8 pin DIL IC holder
	Circuit board
	Battery connector (PP3 type)
	5mm LED holder
	Wire, solder, etc.

Components for Remote Control Receiver (Fig.2.2)

Resistors (all 0.25 watt 5% carbon film)

R1	15k
R2	2M2
R3	4k7
R4	470R
R5	1M8

| R6 | 4k7 |
| R7 | 3k9 |

Potentiometer

| VR1 | 470R min preset |

Capacitors

C1	100μ 16V elect
C2	4n7 polyester
C3	4n7 polyester
C4	33p ceramic plate
C5	220n polyester
C6	220n polyester

Semiconductors

D1	1N4148
D2	1N4148
D3	1N4148
TR1	BPX25 or similar (see text)
TR2	BC559
TR3	BC549
TR4	BC549

Miscellaneous

S1	SPST min toggle
B1	9 volt (six HP7 size cells in plastic holder)
RLA	6 volt coil, 220R or greater coil resistance (see text)
	Circuit board
	Battery clip (PP3 type)
	Wire, solder, etc.

Flash Slave

When a photograph is taken with the aid of a single flashgun it is quite likely to suffer from very harsh and unnatural shadows. This problem can be overcome by using two flashguns. One way of firing the flashguns simultaneously is to use an adaptor lead that permits both guns to connect to the camera's flash contacts. The connecting leads can be rather cumbersome though, and there can be incompatibility problems if you are using flashguns from different manufacturers.

A more satisfactory method is to use a photo-flash slave unit. This is a form of light activated switch which triggers the second flashgun almost instantly when it receives the pulse of light from the primary flashgun. There is obviously some delay between the first and second flashguns being fired, but this is too small to be of any practical consequence. Both of the flashguns are fired while the camera's shutter is fully open.

For this application a relay is too slow, and the flashgun must be controlled via some form of semiconductor switching device. In the past most flash slave units used a thyristor as the switching device. Many electronic flashguns had surprisingly high voltages across their flash-leads, with potentials of around 150 to 200 volts being quite typical. A thyristor was a good choice because high voltage types were readily available at quite low prices. Although not high speed devices by normal electronic standards, thyristors can normally switch on within a microsecond, making them more than adequate for use in a flash slave unit.

Figure 2.3 shows the circuit diagram for a flash slave unit based on a thyristor. The light detector is phototransistor TR1. A phototransistor offers good sensitivity and a reasonably fast operating speed, making it ideal for this application. Although a BPX25 is specified for TR1, the circuit seems to work well using practically any npn silicon phototransistor. The pulse of light from the primary gun causes TR1 to conduct more heavily, which takes its collector lower in voltage. This signal is coupled via C2 to a high gain common emitter amplifier based on TR2. This greatly amplifies and inverts the input signal, giving a large positive change in the potential at its collector. C3 couples this signal to the gate of the thyristor (CSR1), causing the latter to switch on and trigger the secondary flashgun.

A flash slave circuit of this type will still work perfectly well with older electronic flashguns, and some modern types. However, there can be problems when using a thyristor to control many modern flashguns. Unlike a transistor, once switched on a thyristor remains switched on until the anode-

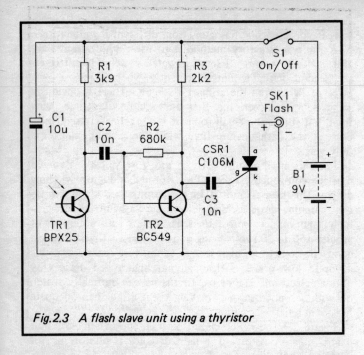

Fig.2.3 A flash slave unit using a thyristor

to-cathode current falls to a low level (typically a few milli-amps). With old-style flashguns a strong pulse of current flows through the thyristor when it is initially triggered, but the current then falls back to a low level, causing the thyristor to switch off.

Modern flashguns almost invariably have a low voltage trigger circuit. After triggering this produces a significant and continuous current flow through the thyristor, and the current flow is often high enough to hold the thyristor in the on state. The circuit triggers correctly when the first photograph of the session is taken, but it refuses to trigger when subsequent photographs are taken. What is actually happening is that the slave unit is, in effect, permanently triggered, and it is preventing the flashgun from recycling properly.

The easiest way around this problem is to use a transistor as the switching device, as in the amended circuit of Figure 2.4. The transistor is pulsed on for long enough to reliably

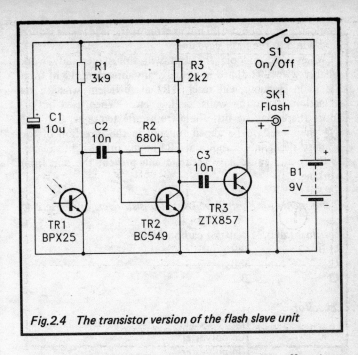

Fig.2.4 The transistor version of the flash slave unit

trigger the secondary flashgun, but it switches off again as soon as the base current subsides. The only problem is that TR3 must be a high voltage device if the unit is to be used with both modern and older flashguns. The ZTX857 specified for TR3 has a collector-to-emitter voltage rating of 300 volts, which should be comfortably higher than the voltage across the trigger circuit of any electronic flashgun. The current consumption of the circuit is about 2 milliamps.

With both the thyristor and transistor versions of the slave unit it is essential to connect the flash-lead to the slave circuit with the polarity shown in the circuit diagrams. A multimeter set to a suitable voltage range should be used to check the polarity of the flash-lead. SK1 is a miniature coaxial connector of the type used for flash sockets on cameras. These can be difficult to obtain, but might be available from larger photographic stores. The easier solution is to buy a short flash extension lead, and remove the appropriate

61

connector plus about 100 millimetres of the lead. This is then hard wired to the flash slave unit.

When used indoors the unit will almost certainly work reliably with TR1 aimed in virtually any direction. Light from the main flashgun will reach TR1 at sufficient strength via reflections from the walls, ceiling, etc. When used out-of-doors there may be little help from reflected light, and TR1 will then need to be aimed roughly in the direction of the primary flashgun. Do not aim TR1 at any bright light sources, as this could cause it to saturate and prevent the unit from working.

Components for Flash Slave Unit (transistor version – Fig.2.4)

Resistors (all 0.25 watt 5% carbon film)
R1	3k9
R2	680k
R3	2k2

Capacitors
C1	10μ 25V elect
C2	10n polyester
C3	10n polyester

Semiconductors
TR1	BPX25 (see text)
TR2	BC549
TR3	ZTX857

Miscellaneous
SK1	Miniature coaxial connector (see text)
B1	9 volt (PP3 size)
S1	SPST min toggle
	Case
	Circuit board
	Wire, solder, etc.

N.B.: To make version shown in Figure 2.3 replace TR3 with CSR1 C106M thyristor.

Enlarger Exposure Meter

This is a device that enables the correct enlarger exposure to be determined without the need for test strips. It is really just a circuit that measures light intensity, but the unit is not calibrated in terms of actual illumination level. The subject of calibration is dealt with later on.

The circuit diagram for the enlarger exposure meter appears in Figure 2.5. It is based on an operational amplifier (IC1), but in this circuit IC1 operates as a voltage comparator. The non-inverting input is fed by R2 and R3 with a reference potential of half the supply voltage. If the potential at the non-inverting input is at a higher potential than this, the output of IC1 goes high and LED indicator D1 is switched on. If the voltage at the non-inverting input is below the reference level, the output of IC1 goes low and D1 is not switched on.

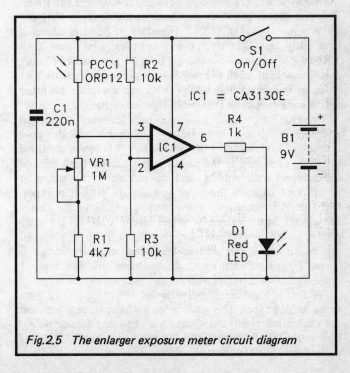

Fig.2.5 The enlarger exposure meter circuit diagram

The non-inverting input is driven from a potential divider circuit that is comprised of PCC1, VR1, and R1. PCC1 is the only component in the upper arm of the potential divider, and it is a cadmium sulphide photoresistor. This is a rather old fashioned type of photocell, but cadmium sulphide cells still have advantages in applications where high operating speed is not required, and this type of cell is a good choice for the present application. The resistance of PCC1 is quite low when it is subjected to high light levels, and can be as low as about 50 ohms. In total darkness its resistance is very high, and is a minimum of 1 megohm. The series resistance of VR1 and R1 form the lower arm of the potential divider.

In use, VR1 is adjusted to find the setting at which the voltage fed to the non-inverting input matches the reference level at the inverting input. In other words, it is adjusted to the point where D1 switches between the on and off states. This changeover point occurs when the resistance of VR1 and R1 is equal to that of PCC1. Therefore, if PCC1 is subjected to a fairly high light level, the switch-over point occurs with VR1 at a low resistance setting. If PCC1 is subjected to only a very low light level, the switch-over point occurs with VR1 close to maximum resistance. VR1 can therefore be fitted with a scale calibrated in terms of light intensity.

One advantage of a cadmium sulphide photoresistor in a simple bridge circuit of this type is that it provides pure resistance. This makes it unnecessary to use a stabilised supply. Variations in the supply voltage affect both sides of the bridge circuit equally, and do not affect the setting at which VR1 balances the input voltages to IC1. It is important that IC1 places only a low level of loading on the photocell circuit, but the use of a device having a MOS input stage produces totally insignificant loading on both potential divider circuits. The current consumption of the circuit is about 2 to 3 milliamps with D1 switched off, and about 5 milliamps more than this with D1 switched on.

VR1 is a logarithmic potentiometer, but it is used here as an antilog type. This gives more uniform spacing between the calibration points than that obtained using a linear potentiometer. It is the centre and left-hand terminals of VR1 (as viewed from the rear) that should be used.

Calibration

In use the meter is placed on the enlarger's baseboard and a diffuser is placed under the lens so that all the light from the lens passes through it, that is, in accordance with the integration principle. The most simple method of calibration is to give VR1 a purely arbitrary scale of letters or numbers. For any particular type of paper you determine the correct exposure time and aperture (for a normally exposed negative) by means of test strips in the normal way. Then, without removing the negative or altering the aperture, you place the meter and the diffuser in position, switch on the enlarger, and rotate the knob of VR1 until the change-over point is located. The scale reading is then written on the paper packet.

For new negatives you keep the exposure time constant and correct the exposure by adjusting the lens aperture to the change-over point of D1. In other words VR1 is preset to the previously determined scale setting, and the lens is adjusted to find the change-over point for D1. It is a good idea to determine two scale settings for two exposure times (say 10 and 30 seconds) for each type of paper, to cater for small and large prints. Alternatively, as several enlarging papers have a constant speed for all grades (except in some instances the highest grade, which requires double the exposure of the others), you can make test strips at various light levels, finding D1's change-over point for each level. The scale is then calibrated directly in exposure times for the one type of paper.

If a different type of paper is used occasionally for any reason, it is possible to determine, again by test strips, a multiplication factor by which scale readings must be corrected for the new paper. In other words, if it is found that the correct exposure for a certain negative and degree of enlargement is say, eight seconds, and the meter indicates ten seconds, then the scale times indicated by other negatives must be multiplied by 0.8.

One final point is that cadmium sulphide cells have very slow response times at low light levels. Having found the change-over point for VR1 it is a good idea to wait a second or two, and then readjust VR1 just in case the value of PCC1 had not properly settled when the original reading was taken.

Resistors (all 0.25 watt 5% carbon film)
R1	4k7
R2	10k
R3	10k
R4	1k

Potentiometer
VR1	1M log carbon

Capacitor
C1	220n polyester

Semiconductors
IC1	CA3130E
D1	5mm red LED

Miscellaneous
PCC1	ORP12 cadmium sulphide photoresistor
B1	9 volt (PP3 size)
S1	SPST min toggle
	Case
	Circuit board
	Large control knob
	Battery connector
	8 pin DIL IC holder
	5mm LED holder
	Wire, solder, etc.

Colour Temperature Meter

A colour temperature meter is quite a simple device that will indicate any bias towards one or other end of the light spectrum in the prevailing lighting conditions. To look at things another way, it compares the amount of blue light with the amount of red light that is present. The information that it provides can be very helpful to photographers as it enables them to compensate for an excess of blue or red light by using suitable camera filters. It should perhaps be pointed out that although one might think that the human eyesight mechanism would be capable of readily detecting changes in colour temperature, this is not really the case. The eye tends to automatically compensate for changes in light conditions, and this makes quite large changes in colour temperature appear quite small.

Of course, a colour film or colour reversal film responds to the actual lighting conditions, and not to the perceived conditions. Thus, for instance, a photograph that is taken indoors using an ordinary tungsten lamp as a light source may well have a considerable red bias unless compensatory filtering is used. Similar experiences with a red or blue hue can occur when outdoor shots are taken, although this is perhaps less of a problem as it can often be used to increase the effectiveness of a photograph. In fact some photographers use filters to enhance colour biases in natural lighting.

The Circuit

The circuit diagram for the colour temperature meter is shown in Figure 2.6. Like the previous project, this one is based on an operational amplifier which is used as a voltage comparator. Also like the previous project, this one uses a form of bridge circuit, with the comparator being used to indicate when the two output voltages from the bridge circuit are balanced. This is again achieved using a LED indicator (D1) to indicate when the change-over point is reached. One half of the bridge is formed by PCC1, VR1, and PCC2. A red filter is placed over PCC1 and a blue filter is used over PCC2.

VR1 performs two functions, one of which is to provide current limiting. This is necessary because the series resistance through the two photocells can be under 100R if they are subjected to high light levels. The second function is to compensate for any mismatch in the sensitivities of the two photocells when they are brightly illuminated. It is also necessary to compensate for any mismatch in their sensitivities when they are subjected to low light levels, but this is achieved by physical means. This process is described in detail later. It is essential to properly compensate for any mismatches in the two photocells as the unit would otherwise respond more readily to changes in light level than it would to changes in

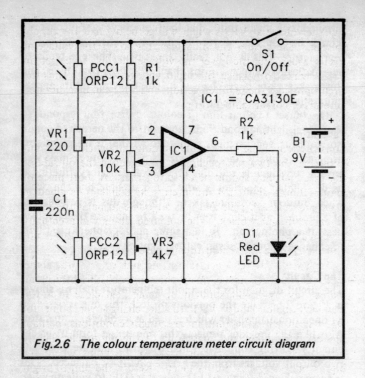

Fig.2.6 The colour temperature meter circuit diagram

colour temperature.

The non-inverting input of IC1 is fed from a potential divider that is comprised of R1, VR2, and VR3. In use, VR2 is adjusted to the change-over point, and the colour temperature is read from a scale marked around VR2's control knob. In other words, it is used in basically the same way as the enlarger exposure meter that was described previously.

If the red light content is stronger than the blue light content, PCC1 will have a lower resistance than PCC2, and the voltage at the wiper of VR1 will go above half the supply voltage. The greater the discrepancy in the relative red and blue light levels, the higher the voltage at VR1's wiper. The higher this voltage, the higher the potential that has to be set on VR2 in order to balance the input voltages to IC1. If the light has a blue bias, PCC2 will have a lower value than PCC1, and the voltage at VR1's wiper will go below half the supply voltage. The greater the blue bias, the lower the voltage at VR1's wiper, and the lower the voltage that has to be set on VR2's wiper to balance the input voltages to IC1. Thus the circuit provides the required action, and VR2 can be calibrated in terms of colour temperature.

Calibration

Construction of the unit should be quite straightforward, but note that the two photocells are mounted on the outside of the case and they should be close together. A short piece of plastic tubing about 20 millimetres in diameter is glued in place around each cell, and it is advisable to paint the inside of each tube matt black. The coloured filters will eventually be glued in place over the top of each tube, but this is not done until some initial adjustments have been made.

Start with VR2 at a central setting and VR3 set for about half maximum resistance. With the photocells brightly illuminated, say by bright sunlight or being held close to a 100 watt light-bulb, adjust VR1 to the change-over point for D1. Then with the unit in less bright conditions, perhaps indoors during daylight, mask one of the photocells slightly in order to bring the circuit back to the point where the input voltages to IC1 are balanced. Return the unit to bright conditions, and readjust VR1 to the change-over point of D1. Then return the unit to dark conditions again, and repeat the procedure until the circuit remains balanced, or very nearly so, whether it is in bright or dull conditions.

The point of this procedure is to make the unit insensitive to changes in light level. It is inevitable that the reading obtained from VR2 will vary slightly with changes in light level, because the two photocells will not have perfectly matched characteristics. Even so, it should be possible to trim out this effect to the point where it becomes insignificant. Probably the best way to mask off the appropriate photocell is by using Bostik Blu-Tack or Plasticine. Trial and error is used to find the cell that needs the masking.

Small disks of blue and red Cellophane are used for the coloured filters, and large sheets of this material can be obtained from stationers. There are other possible materials that can be used here, and there is plenty of room for experimentation. However, be careful not to make the filters too dense, as this seems to prevent the unit from operating correctly. More than one layer of Cellophane is required for each filter, and on the prototype three layers of red Cellophane and two of blue Cellophane were used. This may need to be altered slightly on other units, and the filter densities are adjusted to produce a scale which is neither too cramped to be usable nor so broad that an inadequate range is covered. It is also necessary to ensure that all the required colour temperatures fall within the range of VR2, although adjusting VR3 can correct small errors.

A range of known colour temperatures is needed in order to provide VR2 with a meaningful scale, and the following table should help in this respect.

Source	Colour Temperature (kelvin)
Candle	1900
100W filament lamp	2800
250W filament lamp	2900
500W projector lamp	3200
Photoflood lamp	3350
Direct sunlight (at noon)	5000
Overcast sky (not heavily overcast)	6900
Clear blue sky	10000 to 25000

Components for Colour Temperature Meter (Fig.2.6)

*Resistors (*all 0.25 watt 5% carbon film)

R1	1k
R2	1k

Potentiometers

VR1	220R min preset
VR2	10k lin carbon
VR3	4k7 min preset

Capacitor
C1   220n polyester

Semiconductors
IC1   CA3130E
D1   5mm red LED

Miscellaneous
PCC1   ORP12 cadmium sulphide photoresistor
PCC2   ORP12 cadmium sulphide photoresistor
B1   9 volt (PP3 size)
S1   SPST min toggle
                    Case
                    Circuit board
                    Large control knob
                    Battery connector
                    8 pin DIL IC holder
                    5mm LED holder
                    Filters (see text)
                    Plastic tubing
                    Wire, solder, etc.

Shutter Timer

Testing camera shutters is often carried out with the aid of expensive digital timing equipment, but it is something that can actually be handled quite well using a much more basic timer. The shutter timer featured here has an analogue display provided by an ordinary moving coil meter. It has four ranges with full scale times of 5ms, 50ms, 500ms, and 5 seconds. Most of the more up-market cameras have shutter speeds from about 1/2000th of a second to four seconds, and the unit can therefore be used to check all the shutter speeds of most cameras. It would probably be possible to adapt the unit to suit other automatic timing applications.

The block diagram of Figure 2.7 helps to explain the basic way in which the unit functions. The camera's shutter is placed between a light source and the photocell. The latter feeds into a level detector circuit. Under standby conditions the output of the level detector is low, but when the shutter

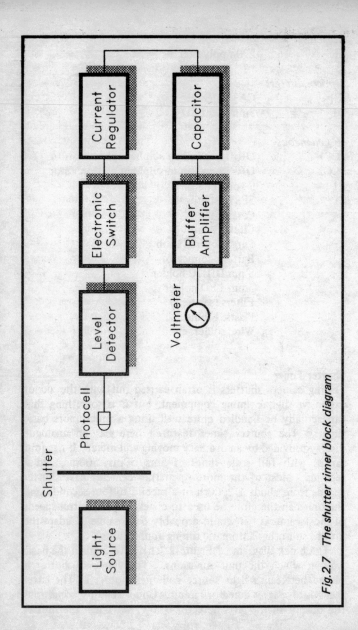

Fig.2.7 The shutter timer block diagram

opens the photocell is subjected to a much higher light level, and this sends the output of the level detector high. The output of the level detector returns to the low state when the shutter closes again. The level detector therefore provides an output pulse of the same duration as the shutter time.

The pulse from the level detector operates an electronic switch, which in turn activates a current regulator circuit. While activated, the current regulator feeds a constant current to a charge storage capacitor. Because the capacitor is charged at a constant current, the charge voltage rises at a linear rate. This voltage is measured by a voltmeter circuit, but a buffer amplifier is needed in order to ensure that the voltmeter does not significantly load the capacitor. Of course, in practice the voltmeter is calibrated in terms of shutter times, and not voltages. The current regulator has four switched output currents, which gives the unit its four measuring ranges.

The Circuit

Figure 2.8 shows the circuit diagram for the shutter timer. The photocell is phototransistor TR1, which offers good sensitivity and a switching speed that is perfectly adequate for this application. IC1 is an operational amplifier, but in this circuit it is used as the voltage comparator in the level detector circuit. R2 and R3 bias the non-inverting input of IC1 to about half the supply voltage. Under standby conditions TR1 has a very high resistance, and the voltage at the inverting input of IC1 is therefore higher than half the supply voltage. This takes the output of IC1 low, which in turn switches off TR2. TR1 receives a much higher light level while the shutter is open, causing its resistance to be much lower, and the voltage fed to the inverting input of IC1 to be pulled below half the supply voltage. This takes the output of IC1 high, and switches on TR2.

TR3 is used as a conventional constant current generator. It has four switched emitter resistors (R7 to R10) which provide the four output currents. R7 to R10 respectively provide the 5ms, 50ms, 500ms, and 5 second ranges. C2 is the charge storage capacitor. While TR2 is switched off, TR3 is also cut off, and no output current flows into C2. When TR2 is switched on, the constant current generator is also

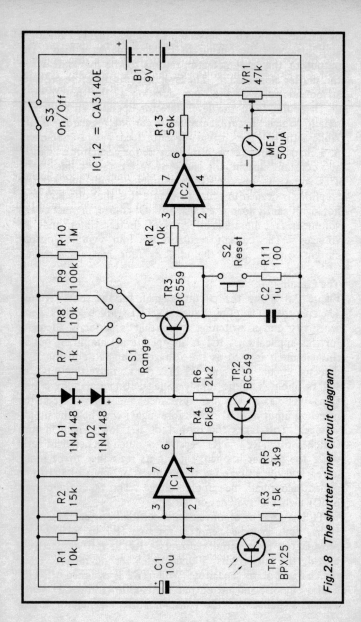

Fig.2.8 The shutter timer circuit diagram

turned on, and the voltage across C2 starts to rise at a linear rate. When TR2 switches off again, TR3 no longer provides an output current, but it does not provide a discharge path for C2 either. The voltmeter circuit is driven by a voltage follower stage based on IC2. The CA3140E used in the IC2 position has a PMOS input stage that has an input impedance of over one million megohms. Consequently, this does not provide a significant discharge path for C2.

The charge on C2, and the reading on ME1, are therefore maintained for some time. Over a period of minutes the reading will probably change significantly due to various leakage resistances in the circuit, but primarily due to the leakage of C2 itself. However, the reading should be accurately maintained for about half a minute or more, which is long enough for the meter to be read. VR1 enables the sensitivity of the voltmeter to be varied, and it acts as the calibration control. The circuit must be manually reset using S2 before a new reading is taken. When operated, S2 simply discharges C2 via current limiting resistor R11. The current consumption of the circuit is about 5 milliamps.

Construction

Construction of the unit is largely straightforward, but there are a couple of points that are worthy of note. C2 should be a good quality capacitor, such as a polyester or polycarbonate type, and not an electrolytic component. TR1 can be virtually any silicon npn phototransistor. Due to the way in which focal plane shutters operate, accuracy is better at the faster shutter speeds if TR1 is a small device, or it is masked to produce a small effective size. Results were best using an SFH305/2, which is a LED-like phototransistor that is only one millimetre wide. This is used vertically with a shutter that runs horizontally, or horizontally with a shutter that runs vertically. The unit will be most convenient to use if TR1 is built into a simple probe type assembly and connected to the main unit via a screened lead up to about 0.5 metres long.

This timer is primarily intended for use with cameras that have focal plane shutters and removable lenses. Test the shutter with the lens removed, the back open, and TR1 close to the shutter curtains. The light source can be a torch, or even the light from a window during daylight hours will probably suffice. The unit will probably function with cameras that do not have removable lenses provided the lenses are used at full aperture, and a strong light source is used. The unit will also work with leaf shutters, but accuracy will not be very good at the highest speeds due to the way in which these shutters operate. The measured shutter speed is likely to be 50 percent or so longer than the effective shutter speed when testing the fastest speed.

Calibration

Start with VR1 at maximum resistance. It is best to calibrate the unit on the 500ms or 5 second range using a camera that is known to be operating with reasonable accuracy. Probably the best method is to set the camera for a shutter speed of ½ second, and to set the timer to the 500ms range. Take a reading in the normal way, and then adjust VR1 for a reading of 500ms. The unit should then provide good accuracy on all four ranges. When using the unit you should bear in mind that camera shutters operate to quite wide tolerances. Modern electronically controlled shutters are generally more accurate than the older clockwork variety, but in either case an error of 20 to 30 percent is not unusual.

Components for Shutter Timer (Fig.2.8)

Resistors (all 0.25 watt 5% carbon film unless noted)

R1	10k
R2	15k
R3	15k
R4	6k8
R5	3k9
R6	2k2
R7	1k 1% metal film
R8	10k 1% metal film
R9	100k 1% metal film
R10	1M 1% metal film
R11	100R
R12	10k
R13	56k

Potentiometer
VR1   47k min preset

Capacitors
C1   10μ 25V elect
C2   1μ polyester

Semiconductors
IC1   CA3140E
IC2   CA3140E
TR1   BPX25 (see text)
TR2   BC549
TR3   BC559
D1   1N4148
D2   1N4148

Miscellaneous
ME1   50μA moving coil panel meter
B1   9 volt (PP3 size)
S1   4 way 3 pole rotary (only one pole used)
S2   Push to make — release to break
S3   SPST min toggle
                   Case
                   Circuit board
                   Control knob
                   Battery clip
                   8 pin DIL IC holder (2 off)
                   Wire, solder, etc.

Chapter 3

MODULATED LIGHT TRANSMISSION

Vast amounts of research and development have gone into modulated light transmission over the last twenty years or so. This "R and D" work has mainly been directed at fibre-optic communications. It is now possible to use fibre optic links over large distances, with each tiny glass filament in the cable carrying vast amounts of data. This type of thing goes well beyond the realm of amateur electronics, but it is still possible for the amateur to construct some useful and interesting equipment which utilizes a fibre-optic cable. Systems which can transmit audio signals and computer data via a fibre optic cable are described in this chapter. Other subjects covered are an opto-isolated audio link, infra-red "cordless" headphones, an infra-red communications system, and a simple modulated light communications system.

Light Link
When I first became interested in electronics, which was back in the 1960s, communicating via a modulated light link was considered to be quite "hi-tech" by those who tried it. In these days of satellite television and compact discs, I suppose that communicating via a beam of light from a torch now has to be considered a rather quaint idea. Although it is now far from the leading edge of technology, modulated light communications remains an interesting field for the experimenter. Because it uses old technology, experimenting with equipment of this type costs very little.

The basic principle of modulated light transmission is very simple. An ordinary filament bulb is driven from a class A power amplifier. With no input signal the bulb is driven at its normal operating voltage. On positive output half cycles it is driven at a higher voltage, and glows more brightly. On negative output half cycles it is driven at reduced voltage, and glows more dimly. Of course, most of the variations in the light output from the bulb occur at a rate which is too high to be perceived by a human observer. As the average power

79

dissipated by the bulb remains unchanged when it is modulated, in theory the light output from the bulb does not noticeably change. In practice there can be low frequency input signals that cause noticeable flickering. Also, because voice signals are often non-symmetrical, the average intensity of the bulb may change slightly when it is modulated.

At the receiving end of the system there is a photoresistor and a load resistor connected across the supply rails. The varying light level is received by the photocell and converted into changes in resistance. These in turn produce changes in the output voltage from the photocell circuit. These voltage changes are unlikely to be particularly large, but a modest amount of amplification produces an output signal that is strong enough to drive a pair of headphones.

A basic modulated light link of this type will work, but it is only fair to point out that is has some major limitations. The maximum range is generally quite respectable, and is largely dependent on the optical system used. Ranges of 60 metres or more can be achieved without resorting to any exotic optics. A system of this type is strictly for "line of sight" operation, so operation over large distances is not very practical anyway.

The main problem with a simple modulated light system is that the audio quality is not very good. One reason for this is that the linearity of the bulb and the photoresistor are not particularly good, which results in significant amounts of distortion. The levels of distortion are less than one might expect though, and the level of fidelity obtained is more than adequate for a speech link.

The more major problem is the limited bandwidth that is obtained. A cadmium sulphide photoresistor does not have a particularly fast response time, particularly when used at very low light levels. However, it would seem to be the light bulb that is the main problem. It obviously takes a finite time for the filament to heat up and cool down, and this seems to produce severe high frequency roll-off. A bandwidth of three kilohertz or so can be achieved, and while this is not good enough for a high quality music link, it is adequate to carry a speech signal.

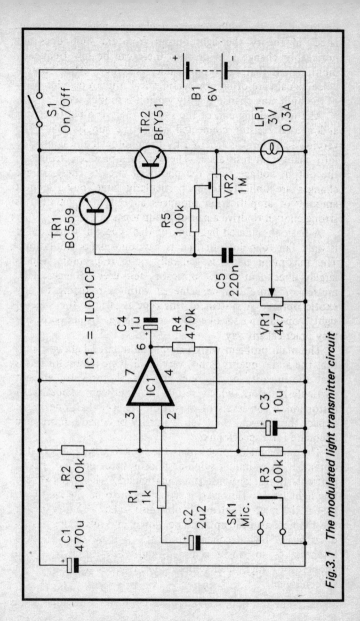

Fig.3.1 The modulated light transmitter circuit

81

The Circuits

Figure 3.1 shows the circuit diagram for the modulated light transmitter. It is designed for use with an inexpensive low impedance dynamic microphone of the type used with cassette recorders. It will also work with higher quality dynamic microphones, and electret microphones, but their higher audio quality is obviously of no advantage in a low-fi application such as this. IC1 is used in the preamplifier stage, and this is a straightforward inverting amplifier having a voltage gain of 470 times. A high level of voltage gain is needed due to the very low output level from a low impedance dynamic microphone. The circuit is powered from a 6 volt supply, so the device used for IC1 must be a type that will operate well on this relatively low supply potential. The TLO81CP will work well in this circuit, but most other operational amplifiers will not. The output from IC1 is coupled to a variable attenuator (VR1), and then to the input of a two stage direct coupled class A amplifier.

TR1 is a common emitter amplifier which has the base-emitter junction of TR2 as its collector load. TR2 is an emitter follower buffer stage which has the light bulb as its emitter load. R5 and VR2 bias the output amplifier, and they also introduce a certain amount of negative feedback over this part of the circuit, which helps to keep the distortion level reasonably low. VR2 enables the quiescent current through the bulb to be varied. It is adjusted to produce an output current that is equal to the bulb's normal operating current.

The prototype has been tried with 3.5 volt bulbs rated at 150mA (0.15A) and 300mA (0.3A). It worked satisfactorily with either type, but as one would expect, results were slightly better when using the higher current bulb. The difference in performance was not particularly large though. It is essential to fit TR2 with a small clip-on heatsink if a 300mA bulb is used.

Figure 3.2 shows the circuit diagram for the modulated light receiver. PCC1 is the cadmium sulphide photocell, and R6 is its load resistor. Virtually any cadmium sulphide cell can be used for PCC1, but there is probably some advantage in using a larger type, such as the ORP12. The audio output signal from the photocell circuit is coupled to the input of a

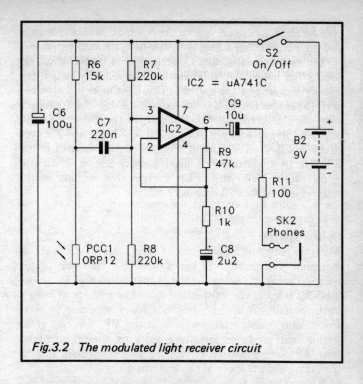

Fig.3.2 The modulated light receiver circuit

non-inverting amplifier based on IC2. This has a closed loop voltage gain of about 50 times (34dB).

It is pointless to use very high gain in this application, as it does not improve the range of the system. The noise level from the photocell circuit tends to be quite high, and this noise limits the useful sensitivity of the receiver circuit. Adding a capacitor of about 1n in parallel with R9 substantially reduces the high frequency noise level, but it might also slightly reduce the already limited high frequency response of the system. It is probably worth adding this capacitor if you have difficulty in obtaining a reasonably good signal to noise ratio from the system.

The output of IC2 is fed to a pair of medium impedance headphones of the type sold as replacements for use with personal stereo units. These should be used with the phones connected in series (i.e. ignore the common earth connection and drive the phones across the other two connections).

The coupling capacitors in both circuits have deliberately been given quite low values in order to roll off the low frequency response of the system. This to some extent counteracts the excessive bass response caused by the frequency response characteristic of the bulb at the transmitter. Results might be improved by making C2, C4, C5, C7 and C9 even lower in value. The current consumption of the transmitter is a little over 150 or 300 milliamps, depending on the current rating of the bulb used. The current consumption of the receiver is only about 2 milliamps.

Optical System

When initially trying out the system, start with VR2 at maximum resistance. LP1 will probably light very dimly when power is applied to the transmitter circuit, but by adjusting VR2 for a lower resistance it should be possible to bring it up to normal brightness. It is not really necessary to make any current measurements when adjusting VR2. Simply give a setting that produces something close to normal brightness from LP1. It is best to err on the side of caution, and use something slightly short of full brightness.

Without some form of optical system this equipment will not operate over a range of more than about two metres or so. One possibility is to use a couple of lenses in the same arrangement used for the infra-red broken beam system described in Chapter 1. An optical system of this type should provide quite good results when applied to this system.

An alternative method, and the one I prefer, is to use the front section of a torch at the transmitter end of the system. Most modern torches seem to have efficient reflectors that produce quite a narrow beam, and give the system a good maximum operating range. If only a moderate range is needed it might not be necessary to use a lens at the receiver. However, it would still be advisable to fit a piece of tubing over PCC1 to shield it from the ambient light. A system of this type can not operate properly if the photocell is subjected to a high level of stray light.

Add a positive lens ahead of PCC1 if the greatest possible operating range is needed. Remember that this will make the receiver highly directional, and that the transmitter and receiver must then be accurately aligned if the system is to operate efficiently. Using a reasonably efficient lens and reflector it should be possible to obtain a range of at least 30 metres, and with everything set up accurately a range of about double this is achievable.

The best setting for VR1 must be found by trial and error. It needs to be well advanced so that something approaching full modulation is used, and a strong audio signal is produced at the receiver. On the other hand, advancing VR1 too far will result in the audio output signal from the transmitter being severely distorted. As described here the system only provides one-way communications. For two-way communications it is necessary to have a transmitter and a receiver at each end of the system.

Components for Modulated Light Transmitter (Fig.3.1)

Resistors (all 0.25 watt 5% carbon film)

R1	1k
R2	100k
R3	100k
R4	470k
R5	100k

Potentiometers

VR1	4k7 log carbon
VR2	1M min preset

Capacitors

C1	470μ 10V elect
C2	2μ2 50V elect
C3	10μ 25V elect
C4	1μ 50V elect
C5	220n polyester

Semiconductors

IC1	TL081CP

TR1	BC559
TR2	BFY51

Miscellaneous

S1	SPST min toggle
LP1	3V 0.15 or 0.3A torch bulb
B1	6 volt (4 × C or D size cells in plastic holder)
SK1	3.5mm jack socket
	Case
	Circuit board
	Reflector or lens (see text)
	Battery connector
	Control knob
	Low impedance dynamic microphone
	Wire, solder, etc.

Components for Modulated Light Receiver (Fig.3.2)

Resistors (all 0.25 watt 5% carbon film)

R6	15k
R7	220k
R8	220k
R9	47k
R10	1k
R11	100R

Capacitors

C6	100μ 10V elect
C7	220n polyester
C8	2μ2 50V elect
C9	10μ 25V elect

Semiconductor

IC2	μA741C

Miscellaneous

S2	SPST min toggle
B2	9 volt (PP3 size)
SK2	3.5mm stereo jack socket

PCC1   ORP12 or similar CDS cell
                    Case
                    Circuit board
                    8 pin DIL IC holder
                    Battery connector
                    Lens or tube (see text)
                    Medium impedance headphones (personal
                    stereo type)
                    Wire, solder, etc.

Audio Isolator

Opto-isolators tend to be regarded as being strictly for transmitting a digital signal, and a typical application is to provide basic on/off control of a triac. A normal opto-isolator consists of an infra-red LED which has its light output directed at a photocell, which is normally a phototransistor. The two components are contained in an opaque case so that the photocell is only subjected to the light from the LED, and is not affected by the ambient light level. If the LED is fed with a current of a few milliamps its light output causes strong leakage currents in the phototransistor, effectively switching it on. The phototransistor can therefore be switched on and off by switching the LED on and off.

The point of this system is that there is no direct electrical connection between the LED and phototransistor. This electrical isolation is important in an application such as control of a mains powered load via a triac, where it is often important that the control circuit is reliably isolated from the dangerous mains supply. Most opto-isolators are rated to withstand voltages of up to 2500V or more between their input and output circuits, making them capable of withstanding any high voltage noise spikes on the mains supply.

There are occasions when it would be useful to pass audio signals through an opto-isolator. This could be where an audio signal must be extracted from a piece of equipment that has a "live" chassis, but more often these days it is where an isolated link is needed in order to keep noise from a digital circuit out of the audio signal path. Electrically isolated links can also be used in order to eliminate problems with "hum"

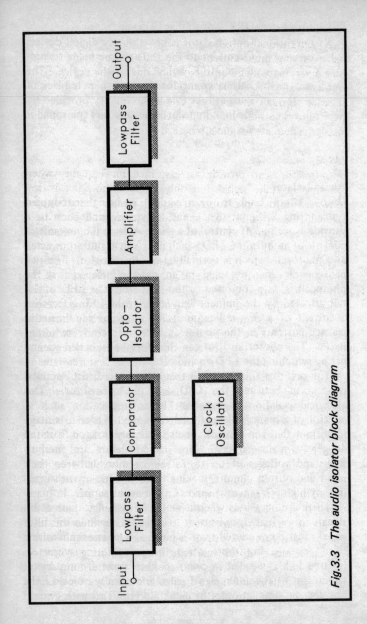

Fig.3.3   The audio isolator block diagram

caused by earth loops.

A conventional opto-isolator is not a purely digital device, and a varying input current to the LED can be made to produce a varying voltage on the output side of the device. The problem with this simple arrangement is that there is a lack of linearity through the device. The audio quality provided by most opto-isolators when used in this way is very poor, and is totally inadequate for most practical purposes.

P.W.M.

Opto-isolators can provide at least medium-fi quality when coupling an audio signal, but only if the audio signal is first converted into some form of digital signal, then coupled through the opto-isolator, and finally converted back to a normal audio signal. This obviously involves a fair amount of signal processing, but because the signal is in digital form when it passes through the opto-isolator, the lack of linearity through the isolator has no effect on the audio quality of the system. The distortion level is governed by the linearity of the analogue to digital and digital to analogue conversion processes.

There are two standard approaches to converting the audio input signal into a digital signal. These are to use either frequency modulation, or pulse width modulation. Frequency modulation is used in some of the projects featured later in this chapter. Here we will consider the pulse width modulation approach. The block diagram of Figure 3.3 helps to explain the way in which this method functions.

The audio input signal is fed to one input of a voltage comparator via a lowpass filter. The audio signal is modulated onto a carrier signal at an ultrasonic frequency, and the purpose of the lowpass filter is to remove any high frequency input signals that could otherwise react with the carrier signal to produce heterodyne tones on the output signal. In many cases there will be no significant high frequency content on the input signal anyway, but it is as well to include this filter just in case. Stray pick up of radio signals by the input wiring can sometimes give problems if the lowpass filtering is omitted.

A clock oscillator drives the other input of the comparator, and this oscillator provides a triangular output waveform. The clock frequency is typically about 80kHz. This arrangement

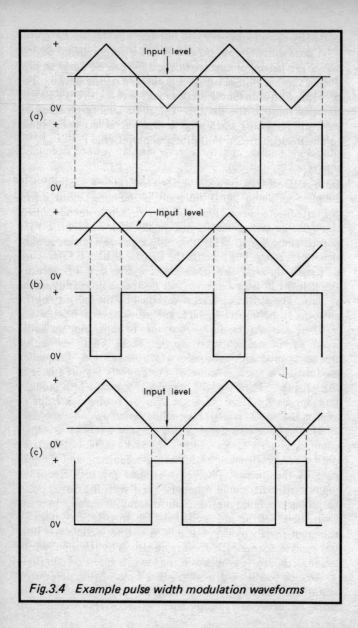

Fig.3.4 Example pulse width modulation waveforms

gives the required pulse width modulation, and the waveforms of Figure 3.4 show the way in which the modulation process operates. In (a) the audio input to the comparator is at its normal quiescent level, which is half way between the peak voltages of the clock signal. The output of the comparator goes high when the input signal is above the clock potential, and low when the input signal is below the clock voltage. This gives a squarewave output signal having a perfect 1 to 1 mark-space ratio, and the average output voltage is equal to half the supply voltage.

In (b) the input level is much higher, and as a result of this the clock signal exceeds the input voltage during only a small part of each clock cycle. This produces much longer output pulses, and the average output voltage is proportionately wider. The input level is very low in (c), and the clock signal is at a higher voltage than the input signal for the majority of the time. This results in an output signal that is a series of short pulses, having a low average output voltage.

The important point to note is that by varying the input voltage, the average output voltage of the comparator is varied as well. Provided the clock signal has good linearity, there is a linear relationship between the input voltage and the average output voltage from the comparator. In order to convert the comparator's pulsing output signal back to an audio signal it is merely necessary to use some lowpass filtering.

Returning to the block diagram of Figure 3.3, the output signal of the comparator is fed through the opto-isolator, and into an amplifier stage. Any lack of linearity through the opto-isolator will not effect the audio output quality, because the opto-isolator is handling a pulse signal. On the other hand, the switching speed of the opto-isolator must be quite fast if it is to provide good results. The linearity of the system is dependent on the output signal switching cleanly and rapidly, with no significant "smearing" of the signal. Remember that it is the mark-space ratio of the output signal that governs the average output voltage, and that even minor interference with the waveform of the pulse signal will degrade the performance of the system.

Unfortunately, opto-isolators are not particularly fast components. By normal electronic standards they are very slow devices indeed. A "bog standard" opto-isolator struggles when fed with a squarewave input signal at a frequency of much more than one or two kilohertz. In the present application the opto-isolator must handle a signal at about 80kHz, and it must maintain the mark-space ratio of the signal. This requires a bandwidth of at least a few hundred kilohertz.

A vast improvement in the switching speed of an opto-isolator can be obtained by using its phototransistor as an emitter follower stage driving a discrete common emitter switch. Some of the more up-market opto-isolators have a built-in common emitter switch. Whether the amplifier stage is integral or discrete, it gives a dramatic improvement in the switching speed, and permits the transfer of squarewave signals at frequencies of several hundred kilohertz. In some cases frequencies in excess of 1MHz can be coupled successfully. This gives a bandwidth that is adequate for the present application.

The final stage of the system is a lowpass filter. In order to produce an output signal that has an insignificant level of clock breakthrough it is necessary for this filter to provide a very high degree of attenuation at the clock frequency. On the other hand, it must not significantly roll-off the higher audio frequencies. This means that a high slope filter must be used, with an attenuation rate of about 40dB per octave being needed to give 80dB of attenuation at the clock frequency, while leaving the audio output signal intact.

The Circuits
Figure 3.5 shows the full circuit diagram for the modulator section of the system. The input filter is a conventional third order (18dB per octave) type based on IC3. Its cutoff frequency is at about 20kHz, and the system therefore covers the full 20Hz to 20kHz audio range. VR1 sets the input bias level, and in practice it is adjusted to optimise the large signal handling capability of the system. This is more a matter of setting the optimum bias level for the comparator than for the filter, and the comparator is driven directly from the output of IC3.

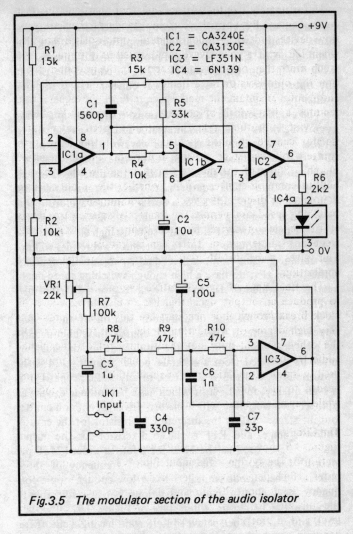

Fig.3.5 *The modulator section of the audio isolator*

IC2 is the comparator, and this is a CA3130E operational amplifier. This is an externally compensated device, but in this case no compensation capacitor is needed because IC2 is used "open loop". In order to work well in this application the comparator must be able to switch at high speed, and an uncompensated CA3130E is more than adequate in this respect. Many other operational amplifiers, including the standard μA741C, will not work properly in this circuit. The LED driven from the output of IC2 is, of course, the LED in the opto-isolator. R6 sets the LED current at just under 3 milliamps.

The clock oscillator is a conventional triangular/squarewave type which uses IC1a as the integrator and IC1b as the trigger. In this case it is only the triangular waveform at the output of IC1a that is required. R1 and R2 provide a bias voltage for the clock oscillator at slightly less than the usual level of half supply voltage. This compensates for slight asymmetry in IC1's output stages, and gives a better output waveform. Due to the high operating frequency of almost 80kHz it is essential to use a device for IC1 that has a suitably high slew rate. The CA3240E is adequate in this respect, but good results will not be obtained using some other dual operational amplifiers. Other types that do have a high enough switching speed might require the value of R1 to be altered to give a different bias level.

The circuit for the demodulator section of the system appears in Figures 3.6 and 3.7. Of course, these circuits have no electrical connection with the modulator circuit, and they must be powered from a separate power supply. IC4 is the opto-isolator, and this is a 6N139, or any similar type. This is a high quality opto-isolator which has a photodiode driving an emitter follower stage which in turn drives a common emitter output stage. R12 is the discrete load resistor for the emitter follower stage, and R11 is the load resistor for the output stage. IC5 is used as the basis for a fourth order (24dB per octave) lowpass filter having a cutoff frequency of about 20kHz. The output from IC5 has a low enough ripple content to be usable in many applications, but it is advisable to also use the additional filter stage of Figure 3.7. This is a third order (18dB per octave) filter, again having a cutoff frequency at about 20kHz. The combined attenuation rate of the two filters is 42dB per octave, which gives about 80dB or so of attenuation at the clock frequency. This reduces the clock breakthrough at the output to less than 1mV peak-to-peak.

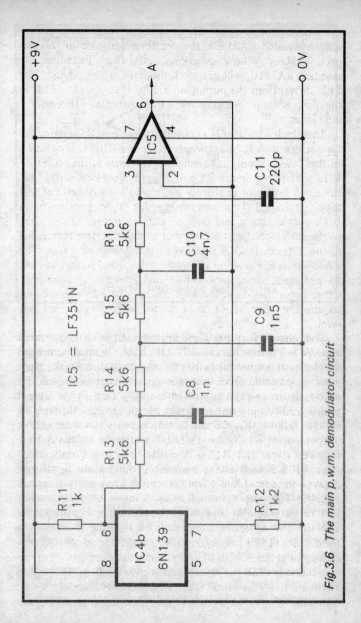

Fig.3.6 The main p.w.m. demodulator circuit

95

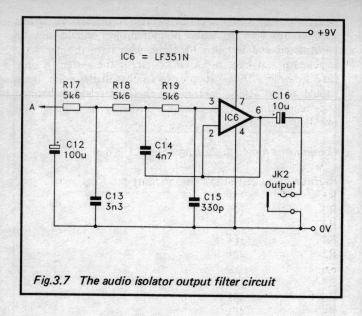

Fig.3.7 The audio isolator output filter circuit

The unit will provide an excellent signal to noise ratio provided it is driven at a fairly high level. A maximum input level of around one to two volts peak-to-peak is ideal. Input levels of much more than about 2 volts peak-to-peak are likely to cause clipping and severe distortion of the output signal. There is a small amount of voltage gain through the circuit incidentally, and the output signal is at almost double the input level. VR1 is adjusted using the standard techniques if suitable test gear is available. If not, simply give it any setting that produces a low distortion output signal with high input levels. While this system does not provide super-fi performance, the signal to noise ratio is excellent and it covers virtually the full audio bandwidth. The distortion performance is quite good, and the system produced no discernible loss of quality when using a good quality FM tuner as the signal source.

If the system is used for mains isolation purposes it is imperative that the person installing the circuit knows exactly what he or she is doing. Errors would be potentially dangerous, and could even have fatal consequences. When used in this way the audio isolator project should only be constructed and installed by those who have the necessary experience and expertise. Of course, if the system is only used to avoid a "hum" loop or to combat digital noise, there should be no safety hazard, and those of relatively limited experience should then have no difficulty in building and installing the system.

Components for Audio Isolator (Figs 3.5, 3.6 & 3.7)

Resistors (all 0.25 watt 5% carbon film)

R1	15k
R2	10k
R3	15k
R4	10k
R5	33k
R6	2k2
R7	100k
R8	47k
R9	47k
R10	47k
R11	1k
R12	1k2
R13 to R19	5k6 (7 off)

Potentiometer

VR1	22k min preset

Capacitors

C1	560p polystyrene
C2	10µ 25V elect
C3	1µ 50V elect
C4	330p polystyrene
C5	100µ 10V elect
C6	1n polyester
C7	33p polystyrene
C8	1n polyester
C9	1n5 polyester
C10	4n7 polyester

C11	220p polystyrene
C12	100μ 10V elect
C13	3n3 polyester
C14	4n7 polyester
C15	330p polystyrene
C16	10μ 25V elect

Semiconductors

IC1	CA3240E
IC2	CA3130E
IC3	LF351N
IC4	6N139N opto-isolator
IC5	LF351N
IC6	LF351N

Miscellaneous

JK1	3.5mm jack socket
JK2	3.5mm jack socket
	Case
	Circuit board
	8 pin DIL IC holder (6 off)
	Wire, solder, etc.

IR Communications Link

The idea of using infra-red for communications purposes is by no means a new idea, and systems for military use have been in existence for more than twenty-five years. In principle the idea is similar to the light beam telephone described previously, but with an infra-red system the beam is invisible. It is probably this invisibility, plus the fact that an infra-red system is virtually tap-proof, that makes systems of this type an attractive proposition for military use. Whether or not infra-red systems have any advantages over other systems in non-military applications is debatable, but they certainly represent an interesting field of operation for the electronics experimenter.

A system of this type could use a simple amplitude modulated beam, like a conventional modulated light link, but the wider bandwidth of infra-red systems permits frequency

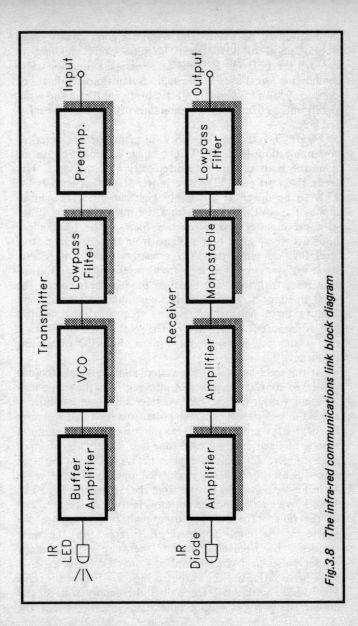

Fig.3.8 The infra-red communications link block diagram

modulation to be used. This enables a good quality audio output signal to be obtained, despite severe non-linearity through the LED and infra-red detector. Like the pulse width modulation signal used in the audio isolator project described previously, an f.m. signal is a form of digital signal, and is not significantly effected by any non-linearity through the infra-red link.

Figure 3.8 shows the block diagram for the infra-red communications link. The VCO (voltage controlled oscillator) is at the heart of the transmitter section of the unit. This feeds the infra-red LED via a buffer stage that enables the LED to be driven at a suitably high current. The control input of the VCO is driven from the microphone via a high gain preamplifier and a lowpass filter. The preamplifier boosts the very weak output signal from the microphone to a level that can drive the VCO properly. The lowpass filter removes input signals at high frequencies which could otherwise react with the VCO signal to produce beat notes. The VCO operates at about 70kHz under quiescent conditions. Positive input half cycles raise its frequency, and negative half cycles reduce its frequency. The greater the input voltage, the greater the increase/reduction in the VCO's operating frequency.

At the receiving end of the system an infra-red photodiode is used to convert the pulses of infra-red from the transmitter to small voltage pulses. A two stage high gain amplifier is needed in order to boost these pulses to a level that will drive the next stage properly. This is a monostable, and it produces a pulse of fixed duration each time it is triggered by an input pulse. Figure 3.9 helps to explain the way in which this stage demodulates the frequency modulated input signal.

In Figure 3.9(a) the output from the monostable has a 1 to 3 mark-space ratio, and the output is in the high state for 25% of the time. The average output voltage is therefore one quarter of the supply potential. In Figure 3.9(b) the input frequency has been doubled, and there are twice as many output pulses in a given period of time. This gives a 1 to 1 mark-space ratio, and the output is high for 50% of the time. The average output voltage is half the supply voltage, and double the previous output potential. In other words, the

100

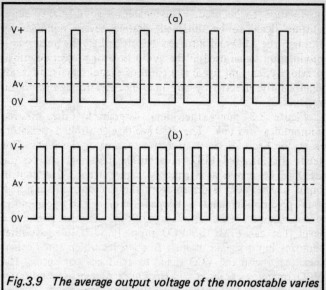

Fig.3.9 The average output voltage of the monostable varies with changes in the input frequency

average output voltage of the monostable is proportional to the input frequency, and the required frequency-to-voltage conversion is being provided. The output signal is a pulsed type, but a lowpass filter is all that is needed in order to smooth out the pulses and recover the original audio signal. Although this is a very simple form of demodulator, with a low frequency f.m. signal it actually works quite well, and provides surprisingly good linearity.

The Circuits

The circuit diagram for the transmitter appears in Figure 3.10. The microphone preamplifier is a two stage common emitter type using TR2 and TR3. The lowpass filtering is provided by feedback capacitors C4 and C6. These considerably attenuate the higher audio frequencies, but these are not required for a voice link. Rolling off the upper audio response gives a significant improvement in the system's signal to noise ratio. The amplifier is designed to operate with a low impedance

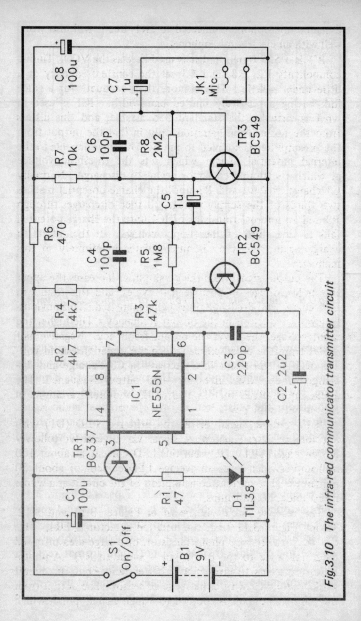

Fig.3.10 The infra-red communicator transmitter circuit

dynamic microphone connected to JK1, but it will also work well with an electret microphone.

IC1 is a 555 timer, and it is used here as the VCO. Timing components R2, R3, and C3 set the centre frequency at a little under 40kHz. This is more than adequate for a voice link having a relatively limited bandwidth. IC1 is used in what is virtually the standard 555 astable, and this differs from the normal configuration only in that the output from the preamplifier is coupled to pin 5. This pin connects to the internal potential divider which sets the threshold voltage at which the timing capacitor begins to discharge. Normally C3 charges via R2 and R3 until the charge potential reaches two thirds of the supply voltage. It then discharges through R3 and an internal transistor of IC1 until the charge potential falls to one third of the supply voltage. It then starts to charge again, and the circuit oscillates indefinitely in this manner.

The output signal from the preamplifier increases the upper threshold voltage on positive half cycles, and this results in C3's charge and discharge times being increased. This obviously gives a reduction in the output frequency. The higher the input voltage, the lower the output frequency. Negative half cycles from the preamplifier reduce the upper threshold voltage of IC1, and result in a decrease in C3's charge and discharge times. This gives increased output frequency. The audio input signal therefore gives the required variations in the output frequency.

IC1's output signal drives the infra-red LED (D1) with a (more or less) squarewave signal via an emitter follower buffer stage (TR1). R1 sets the LED current at about 100 milliamps, which gives an average LED current of about 50 milliamps. The current consumption of the circuit as a whole is just under 60 milliamps.

The receiver circuit is shown in Figures 3.11 and 3.12. Taking Figure 3.11 first, the infra-red detector is TR4. This can be virtually any phototransistor, or a large area infra-red diode (cathode to the 0 volt rail – anode to R9). A phototransistor seems to give slightly better range, but the circuit works quite well with either type of sensor. The output from the photocell circuit is coupled to a high gain amplifier which

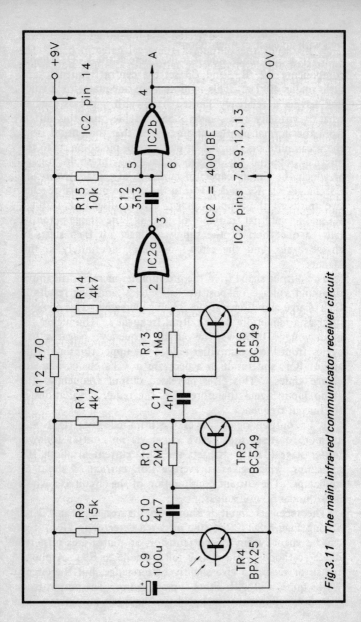

Fig.3.11 The main infra-red communicator receiver circuit

104

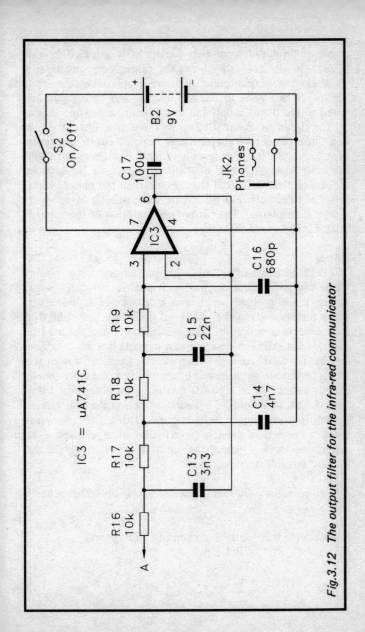

Fig.3.12 The output filter for the infra-red communicator

has TR5 and TR6 as common emitter amplifiers. The monostable is produced from two CMOS NOR gates (IC2a and IC2b). It has R15 and C12 as the timing components, and these set the output pulse duration at approximately 20μs. The other two gates in IC2 are unused, but their inputs are wired to the 0 volt supply rail to prevent spurious operations.

The circuit of Figure 3.12 is for the output filter, and this is a 24dB per octave lowpass filter having a cutoff frequency of just over 3kHz. This gives over 80dB of attenuation at the clock frequency. A pair of medium impedance headphones are driven from JK2, and they should have the phones wired in series. The output of the circuit is also suitable for use with a crystal earphone. The current consumption of the receiver circuit is just over 5 milliamps.

Optics
The built-in lenses of the LED and phototransistor or photodiode will not provide the unit with a particularly large range. In fact it will probably work over a distance of no more than a few metres unless some additional optics are used. All that is needed is a couple of low cost plastic lenses, as used in some of the infra-red broken beam projects that are described in Chapter 1. These are used in exactly the same way as the lenses in the broken infra-red beam projects, and they should permit a range of at least 30 metres to be obtained. Using large lenses it should be possible to obtain a much greater operating range, but it then becomes difficult to get everything accurately aligned. Nevertheless, it is interesting to experiment with a few lenses in an attempt to obtain the greatest possible operating range.

Components for Infra-Red Communications Link Transmitter (Fig.3.10)

Resistors (all 0.25 watt 5% carbon film unless noted)

R1	47R 1 watt
R2	4k7
R3	47k
R4	4k7
R5	1M8

R6	470R
R7	10k
R8	2M2

Capacitors

C1	100μ 10V elect
C2	2μ2 50V elect
C3	220p polystyrene
C4	100p ceramic plate
C5	1μ 50V elect
C6	100p ceramic plate
C7	1μ 50V elect
C8	100μ 10V elect

Semiconductors

IC1	NE555N
TR1	BC337
TR2	BC549
TR3	BC549
D1	TIL38 or similar

Miscellaneous

S1	SPST min toggle
B1	9 volt (6 × HP7 size cells in holder)
JK1	3.5mm jack socket
	Case
	Circuit board
	Lens (see text)
	8 pin DIL IC holder
	Low impedance dynamic microphone
	Battery connector (PP3 type)
	Wire, solder, etc.

Components for Infra-Red Communications Link Receiver (Figs 3.11 & 3.12)

Resistors (all 0.25 watt 5% carbon film)

| R9 | 15k |
| R10 | 2M2 |

R11	4k7
R12	470R
R13	1M8
R14	4k7
R15 to R19	10k (5 off)

Capacitors

C9	100µ 10V elect
C10	4n7 polyester
C11	4n7 polyester
C12	3n3 polyester
C13	3n3 polyester
C14	4n7 polyester
C15	22n polyester
C16	680p polystyrene
C17	100µ 10V elect

Semiconductors

IC2	4001BE
IC3	µA741C
TR4	BPX25 (see text)
TR5	BC549
TR6	BC549

Miscellaneous

S2	SPST min toggle
B2	9 volt (PP3 size)
JK2	3.5mm stereo jack socket
	Case
	Circuit board
	Battery connector
	8 pin DIL IC holder
	14 pin DIL IC holder
	Lens (see text)
	Medium impedance headphones
	Wire, solder, etc.

"Cordless" Headphones

So-called "cordless" headphones have become quite popular in recent years, and seem to be regarded by many as a new idea. However, I first experimented with this type of equipment in 1977, and even then it was not a brand new idea. At that time it was difficult to get good results as the infra-red emitters and detectors available in those days were less than ideal for this application. They were also relatively expensive. These days it is much easier to produce a practical system, and for a simple monophonic system the cost is quite reasonable.

For those who are unfamiliar with this type of equipment it should perhaps be explained that "cordless" headphones connect to a small unit about the size of a personal stereo. This unit is actually an infra-red receiver. The matching transmitter connects to the headphone socket of (say) a television set, and couples the audio signal from the television set to the receiver unit via a frequency modulated infra-red signal. This avoids having a long cable trailing from the listener to the television or other signal source, and eliminates accidents with people tripping over the cable. It also avoids standing up and discovering with a sudden jerk that you are standing on the headphone cable!

In essence a cordless headphone system is very similar to the infra-red communications system described previously, but there are a few differences in points of detail. An important difference is that the system must not be highly directional. The transmitter must cover a reasonably large field so that you are not restricted to sitting in one particular spot. A reasonably wide area of coverage also makes it possible for two or more users to make use of the system. Another difference is that the system must cover the full audio range, or something close to it, so that both speech and music signals can be handled properly.

The Circuits

The transmitter circuit appears in Figure 3.13. IC1 is a buffer stage which provides an input impedance of 50k. It provides an output impedance that is low enough to drive the next stage properly, and the next stage is a third order lowpass

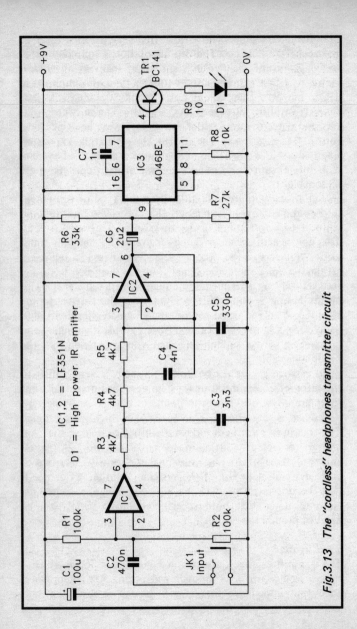

Fig.3.13 The "cordless" headphones transmitter circuit

filter based on IC2. The cutoff frequency of this filter is approximately 20kHz. The output of IC2 is coupled to the control input of the VCO. The latter uses the oscillator section of IC3, which is a CMOS 4046BE "micropower" phase locked loop. In this circuit only the VCO section of this device is utilized, and no connections are made to the phase comparators, etc. R6 and R7 provide a bias voltage to IC3's control input. C7 and R8 are the timing components, and they give a centre frequency of just under 80kHz.

A good quality squarewave output signal is produced at pin 4 of IC3, and this drives the infra-red LED (D1) via an emitter follower buffer amplifier (TR1). D1 must not be an ordinary infra-red LED of the type used in infra-red remote control systems. R9 sets the LED current at almost 500 milliamps, which gives an average LED current of 250 milliamps. D1 must be a high power infra-red LED that can handle an average current of at least 250 milliamps. I used the Maplin "GaAs Infra-Red Photo Emitter" (cat. no. KW66W), but any similar device of adequate current rating should work just as well. Alternatively, five ordinary 5 millimetre infra-red LEDs can be used. These should have individual 47R current limiting resistors, as shown in Figure 3.14. This method might actually be cheaper than using a single high power LED, but a high power LED seems to give slightly better results, and is a more convenient way of handling things.

The receiver circuit diagram is shown in Figures 3.15 and 3.16. Figure 3.15 shows the circuit for the amplifier and monostable stages. This circuit is very much the same as its equivalent in the infra-red communications system, but there are a couple of important differences. In order to obtain good results with a low noise level I would not recommend using a phototransistor as the photocell in this case. A large area infra-red photodiode which does not have a built-in lens gives good results, and is largely non-directional.

Two of these diodes in series gives a significant improvement in the signal to noise ratio when the system is used over a range of three to four metres. In fact I would recommend the use of four diodes in parallel if the system is going to be used over a range of about 4 metres or so. The system will

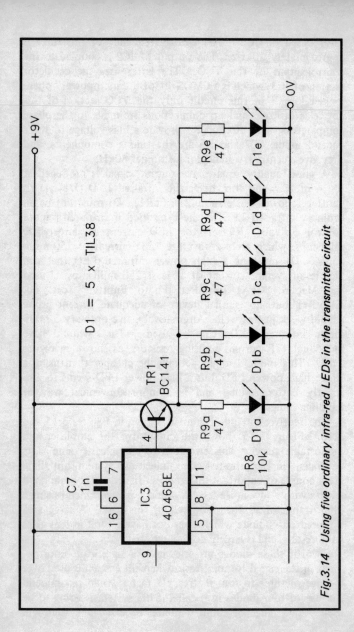

Fig.3.14 Using five ordinary infra-red LEDs in the transmitter circuit

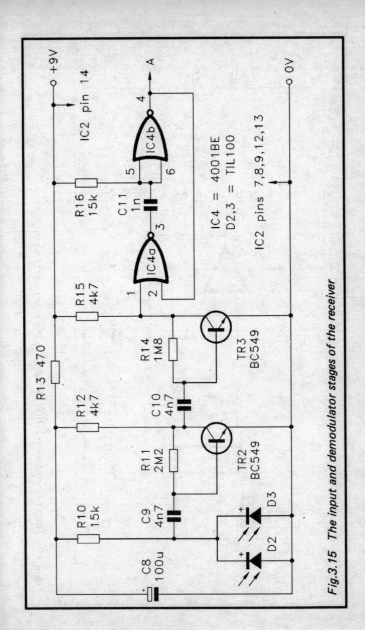

Fig.3.15 The input and demodulator stages of the receiver

113

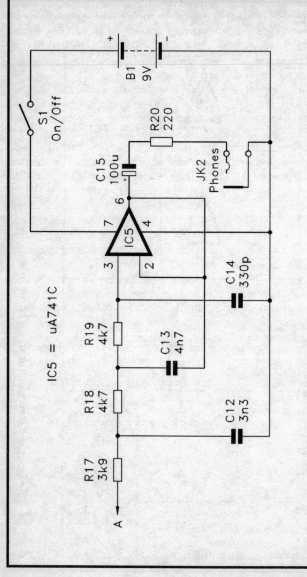

Fig.3.16 The receiver output filter circuit

114

operate over a range of more than 5 metres, but even using four photodiodes in the receiver the signal to noise ratio is unlikely to be satisfactory over a range of more than about 5 metres. Presumably the system will mostly be used over a range of about 3 metres, and it should give very good noise performance over this sort of range.

The values of the timing components in the monostable have been altered to give a shorter pulse duration. This is necessary because of the higher carrier frequency used in this case. The output filter (Fig.3.16) is an 18dB per octave type having a cutoff frequency at about 20kHz. This does not provide a tremendous amount of attenuation at the carrier frequency, and the actual level of attenuation is about 36dB. However, a certain amount of carrier breakthrough is of no great consequence in this case, and will not have a detrimental effect on the performance of the headphones. Medium impedance headphones should be used, and the two phones should be connected in series. The current consumption of the circuit is about 5 milliamps.

Construction of these circuits is reasonably straightforward, but the 4046BE is a CMOS device, and the normal anti-static handling precautions should therefore be observed when dealing with this component. TR1 will operate quite hot, and it is a good idea to fit it with a small clip-on heatsink.

Components for "Cordless" Headphones – Transmitter (Fig.3.13)

Resistors (all 0.25 watt 5% carbon film unless noted)

R1	100k
R2	100k
R3	4k7
R4	4k7
R5	4k7
R6	33k
R7	27k
R8	10k
R9	10R 2 watt

Capacitors

C1	100μ 10V elect
C2	470n polyester
C3	3n3 polyester
C4	4n7 polyester
C5	330p polystyrene
C6	2μ2 50V elect
C7	1n polyester

Semiconductors

IC1	LF351N
IC2	LF351N
IC3	4046BE
TR1	BC141
D1	High power IR LED (see text)

Miscellaneous

JK1	3.5mm jack socket
	Case
	Circuit board
	Clip-on heatsink for TR1
	8 pin DIL IC holder (2 off)
	16 pin DIL IC holder
	Wire, solder, etc.

*Components for "Cordless" Headphones — Receiver
(Figs 3.15 & 3.16)*

Resistors (all 0.25 watt 5% carbon film)

R10	15k
R11	2M2
R12	4k7
R13	470R
R14	1M8
R15	4k7
R16	15k
R17	3k9
R18	4k7
R19	4k7
R20	220R

Capacitors

C8	100μ 10V elect
C9	4n7 polyester
C10	4n7 polyester
C11	1n polyester
C12	3n3 polyester
C13	4n7 polyester
C14	330p polystyrene
C15	100μ 10V elect

Semiconductors

IC4	4001BE
IC5	μA741C
TR2	BC549
TR3	BC549
D2	TIL100 or similar
D3	TIL100 or similar

Miscellaneous

S1	SPST min toggle
B1	9 volt (PP3 size)
JK2	3.5mm stereo jack socket
	Case
	Circuit board
	8 pin DIL IC holder
	14 pin DIL IC holder
	Battery connector
	Medium impedance headphones
	Wire, solder, etc.

Fibre Optics

Fibre-optics enable minute cables to carry vast amounts of data. For commercial users this factor is probably the most important one, but there are other advantages to using an optical cable. One of these is that an optical cable is completely immune to stray pick-up of radio signals, mains "hum", and other electrical noise. In a similar vein, a fibre-optic cable, even if it is carrying vast amounts of data, does not radiate any electrical noise. It follows from this that

117

there is no problem with "crosstalk", where the signal in one cable is picked up by a second cable running alongside it. Obviously light could leak from one cable to another, but practical optical cables have an opaque outer sleeving which prevents any light leaks. Other advantages include reduced fire hazard (there are no electrical signals to cause sparks or over-heating), and electrical isolation between the transmitter and receiver.

Obviously there are also disadvantages to optical cables. Not the least of these is that you can not simply connect the output of an electronic circuit to one end of the cable, and extract an electrical signal at the other end. A photocell plus some electronics are needed at each end of the cable, which increases costs. Fibre-optic cables have a minimum bend radius, which is usually about 50 to 80 millimetres. They can be inefficient if taken through a tighter radius than the recommended minimum, and can even sustain damage. Whatever their advantages and disadvantages, fibre-optic links certainly represent an interesting field for the electronics experimenter.

Cable Basics

Although many people seem to be under the impression that a fibre-optic cable is just a filament of glass having an opaque outer sleeving, things are actually a little more complicated than this. These days the glass filament is more likely to be polymer than glass, and the usual arrangement is outlined in Figure 3.17. There is a central core having a high refractive index, and an outer cladding having a low refractive index. Reflection where the inner core and the cladding meet enables light to travel along the cable by effectively bouncing from wall to wall. It is this bouncing that enables the cable to act as a light guide, taking the light around corners and bends.

The angle at which light is reflected depends on the characteristics of the cable and the angle at which light enters the cable. In Figure 3.17 the light ray is subjected to "high order mode" propagation, but light entering at a more shallow angle would bounce off the wall of the cable at a much shallower angle, and would consequently travel much further per bounce. This is termed "low order mode" propagation.

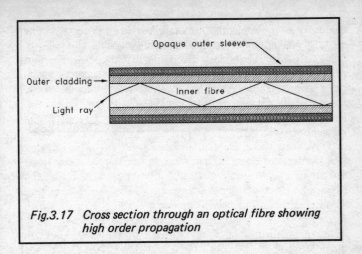

Fig.3.17 *Cross section through an optical fibre showing high order propagation*

The practical importance of these two modes is that light travelling along the cable in the high order mode has to travel much further than light which is propagated in the low order mode. This smears signals sent down the cable, and limits the maximum frequency that can be accommodated. This is only of significance in very wide bandwidth links though, and with the systems we will consider here it is not a practical consideration. So-called "single mode" cables are designed to support only one propagation mode, but it is not necessary to use a single mode cable with the fibre-optic projects described in this book.

There is an alternative type of cable called "graded index" cable (as opposed to the normal "stepped index" type). This is actually quite similar to the stepped index variety, but there is a gradual change from a high refractive index at the centre to a low refractive index close to the sleeving. This results in the light travelling down the cable in much the same way as described previously, but with the light taking a curved route, as in Figure 3.18.

The standard size for fibre-optic cables is an overall diameter of 2.2 millimetres, with a fibre diameter of 1 millimetre. There are three basic ways of using this cable. One is to use ordinary LEDs and photocells, and to improvise your own

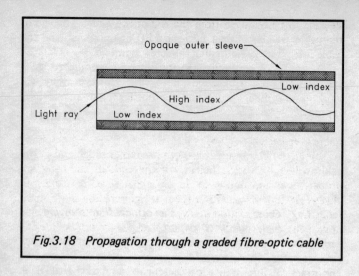

Opaque outer sleeve

Low index

High index

Light ray

Low index

Fig.3.18 Propagation through a graded fibre-optic cable

ways of aligning the ends of the cable with the LED and the photocell. This is only likely to work well if both the LED and the photocell have built-in lenses that make them quite directional.

The second method is to again use ordinary LEDs and photocells, but to use them with the special connectors that are available. A typical connector system consists of a plug which fits onto the end of the cable, and a socket which is mounted on the circuit board. The socket has an aperture into which a LED or photocell will fit. This method ensures good alignment of the LED and photocell with the cable, but can be relatively expensive.

I would certainly recommend the third option, which is to use special LEDs and photocells that are designed specifically for use with fibre-optic cables. The SFH350 phototransistor and SFH750 LED are very easy to use. They each have an aperture which will take a standard 2.2 millimetre fibre-optic cable, and the ends of the cable do not need any special preparation. The MFOE71 LED and MFOD71 photodiode are also quite easy to use. These have a sort of screw terminal arrangement which requires a few millimetres of the outer sleeving to be removed from the end of the cable. The end of the cable is then pushed into the LED or photocell, and the cable is secured by tightening the screw terminal.

The projects featured here are designed to operate using special fibre-optic LEDs and photocells. However, they will work using ordinary LEDs and photocells provided everything is properly aligned.

Cable Preparation

As supplied, fibre-optic cable often has rather rough ends. The cable will only work efficiently if the ends of the cable are properly cut and polished. In my experience the cable will always give good results if it is cut at right angles using a sharp modelling knife. Cut cleanly through the cable in a single movement using plenty of pressure on the knife. A fine file can be used to polish the ends of a cable, but this should not be necessary if it has been cut properly in the first place. It is important that the cut is made perpendicular to the cable, as an angled cut will tend to shift the optimum angle of light entry off its normal end-on angle.

Removing some of the outer sleeving from the end of a cable can be a little more tricky. You must take great care not to seriously damage the polymer fibre when doing this. Apart from weakening the cable, damaging the polymer fibre can greatly reduce the efficiency of the cable. Ordinary wire strippers can sometimes be very effective when used with fibre optic cables, but some types do not seem to give good results. A method that often works well is to make a slit along the full length of the piece of sleeving that must be removed. This requires a sharp knife, with due care being taken not to cut too deep and not to slip and cut yourself or the worktop, since the small round shape of fibre-optic cables makes them a little difficult to work with. Once this cut has been made it is quite easy to peel back the piece of sleeving and trim if off using the knife.

Audio Link

An audio signal can be sent down a fibre-optic cable using the same frequency modulation technique used in the infra-red communicator and "cordless" headphones described previously.

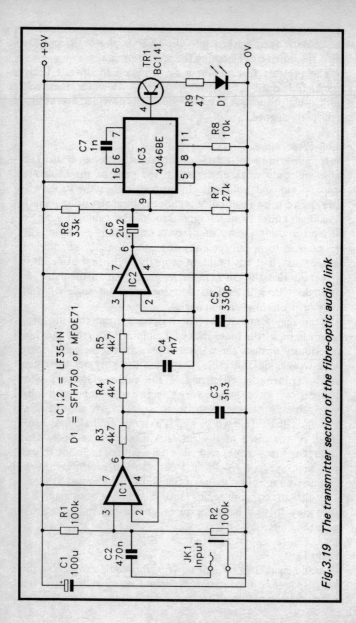

Fig.3.19 The transmitter section of the fibre-optic audio link

122

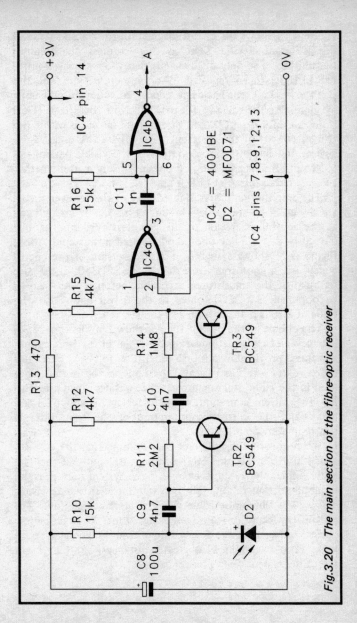

Fig.3.20 The main section of the fibre-optic receiver

123

Figure 3.19 shows the circuit diagram for the transmitter, and this is essentially the same as the "cordless" headphones transmitter. The only difference is that the high power infrared LED has been replaced by a fibre-optic type, and the average LED current has been reduced to about 50 milliamps by increasing the value of R9 to 47R. Note that the SFH750 is not an infra-red LED, and that its light output is within the visible red part of the spectrum. The MFOE71 is an infra-red device, and has little or no output in the visible part of the spectrum. In this application it does not really matter whether a visible red or infra-red LED is used.

The amplifier and monostable stages of the receiver circuit are shown in Figure 3.20. This circuit is again much the same as the equivalent section of the "cordless" headphones, but obviously just the one photodiode is used in this application. Figure 3.21 shows a slightly modified version of the circuit which uses a phototransistor, such as the SFH350. If the base terminal of the transistor is accessible, better results seem to be obtained if it is connected to the 0 volt rail. Also, the value of R10 is reduced from 15k to 3k9.

The circuit of the output filter is shown in Figure 3.22. A high level of carrier attenuation is needed in this application, and this is provided by a fourth order filter followed by a third order filter. This is basically the same as the output filter used in the audio isolator project that was described previously. The current consumption of the receiver is about 6 milliamps, and the current consumption of the transmitter is approximately 55 milliamps.

When constructing the unit bear in mind that the 4046BE and 4001BE are both CMOS components, and that they are both vulnerable to static charges. The system only provides monophonic operation, but two transmitters, two receivers, and a twin fibre-optic cable will give stereo operation. The circuit was found to work well using 20 metres of fibre-optic cable. It would almost certainly provide a good signal to noise ratio over somewhat greater distances, but I have not tested the system using a longer cable.

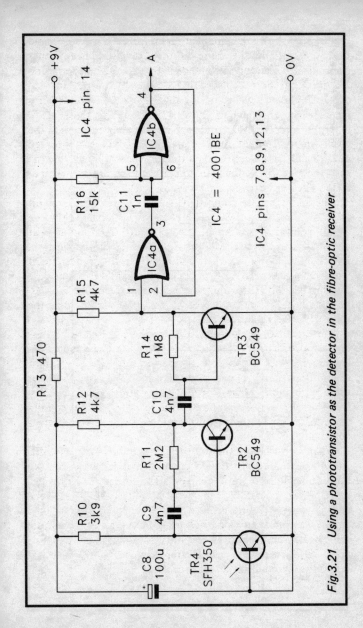

Fig.3.21 Using a phototransistor as the detector in the fibre-optic receiver

125

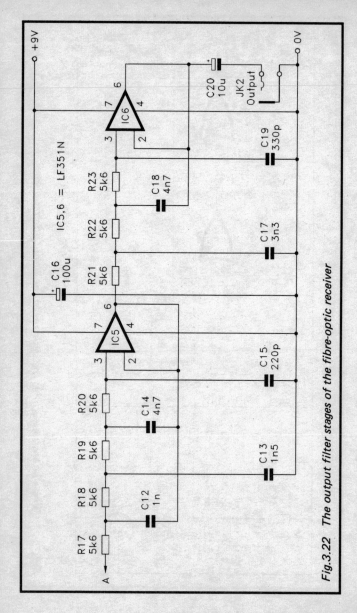

Fig.3.22 The output filter stages of the fibre-optic receiver

126

Components for Fibre-Optic Audio Link — Transmitter (Fig.3.19)

Resistors (all 0.25 watt 5% carbon film unless noted)

R1	100k
R2	100k
R3	4k7
R4	4k7
R5	4k7
R6	33k
R7	27k
R8	10k
R9	47R 1 watt

Capacitors

C1	100μ 10V elect
C2	470n polyester
C3	3n3 polyester
C4	4n7 polyester
C5	330p polystyrene
C6	2μ2 50V elect
C7	1n polyester

Semiconductors

IC1	LF351N
IC2	LF351N
IC3	4046BE
TR1	BC141
D1	SHF750 or MFOE71 (see text)

Miscellaneous

JK1	3.5mm jack socket
	Case
	Circuit board
	8 pin DIL IC holder (2 off)
	16 pin DIL IC holder
	Wire, solder, etc.

Components for Fibre-Optic Audio Link – Receiver
(Figs 3.20 & 3.22)

Resistors (all 0.25 watt 5% carbon film)

R10	15k
R11	2M2
R12	4k7
R13	470R
R14	1M8
R15	4k7
R16	15k
R17 to R23	5k6 (7 off)

Capacitors

C8	100μ 10V elect
C9	4n7 polyester
C10	4n7 polyester
C11	1n polyester
C12	1n polyester
C13	1n5 polyester
C14	4n7 polyester
C15	220p polystyrene
C16	100μ 10V elect
C17	3n3 polyester
C18	4n7 polyester
C19	330p polystyrene
C20	10μ 25V elect

Semiconductors

IC4	4001BE
IC5	LF351N
IC6	LF351N
TR2	BC549
TR3	BC549
D2	MFOD71 (see text)

Miscellaneous

JK2	3.5mm jack socket
	Case

Circuit board
8 pin DIL IC holder (2 off)
14 pin DIL IC holder
Standard 2.2/1mm fibre-optic cable
Wire, solder, etc.

If a phototransistor is used, delete D2 and add:-
TR4   SFH350
Also, change the value of R10 to 3k9.

Fibre-Optic Data Link

When interconnecting computers via their RS232C serial ports there can be problems with earth loops and radio frequency interference being radiated. A fibre-optic data link avoids both problems, and it is not difficult to produce a system that can handle baud rates up to the normal maximum of 19200 baud. One way of tackling the problem is to use the serial input signal to directly gate the transmitting LED on and off. A detector circuit and DC amplifier would then be used at the receiver to detect the pulses of light and convert them back into a serial signal at the appropriate voltage level.

There is a drawback to this system in that the output from the detector circuit would almost certainly be at a very low level unless quite expensive emitter and detector devices were used. This would make it difficult to obtain good reliability and long term stability. Better results can be obtained using a frequency modulation system, much like the system used in the fibre-optic audio link described previously. However, in this application things can be simplified somewhat as there are only two signal levels (logic 1 and logic 0) to contend with. The carrier wave is therefore switched between two frequencies, with each frequency representing a different logic level. This is basically the same system that is used for modems, and many other types of data link.

The block diagram of Figure 3.23 outlines the way in which this system functions, and it has obvious similarities to the fibre-optic audio link described previously. A VCO again forms the basis of the transmitter, with its output driving the LED via a buffer stage. The input signal is a logic type, but

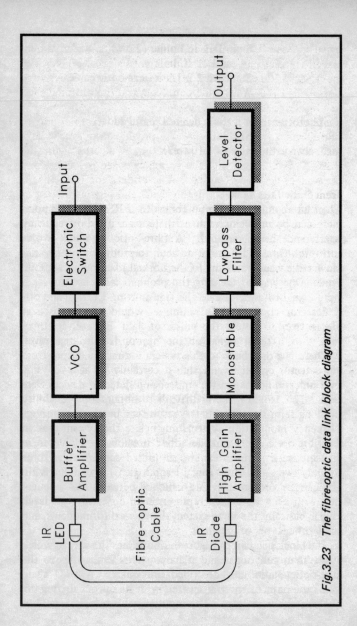

Fig.3.23 The fibre-optic data link block diagram

an RS232C signal is not at normal 5 volt logic levels. The input signal is nominally at plus and minus 12 volts, but minimum loaded voltages of plus and minus 3 volts are acceptable. The input signal is used to drive an electronic switch. The switch closes when the input signal goes high, and this pulls the VCO to a higher operating frequency.

At the receiver there is again a high gain amplifier, monostable, and a lowpass filter. These provide an output voltage that switches between two levels in sympathy with the RS232C input signal, but the switching speed is too low and the voltage levels are wrong. A level detector is all that is needed in order to speed up the signal and provide an output signal at suitable voltages. With an RS232C signal it is important to accurately maintain the mark-space ratio of the input signal, and any slight smearing of the signal is likely to give corrupted data. The switching threshold of the level detector must therefore be set half-way between the maximum and minimum otuput voltages from the lowpass filter.

The Circuits
Figure 3.24 shows the full circuit diagram for the transmitter section of the fibre-optic data link. Like the infra-red communications transmitter described previously, it is based on a 555 timer (IC1) which acts as the VCO. It drives an LED via an emitter follower buffer stage based on TR2. R4 sets the LED current of about 60 milliamps, which gives an average LED current of around 30 milliamps. The overall current consumption of the circuit is about 36 milliamps incidentally.

TR1 is the electronic switch that is controlled by the RS232C input signal. When the input is negative, TR1 is cut off and the potential divider formed by R2 and R3 pulls the control input of IC1 slightly higher than normal. This gives a slightly lower output frequency. When the input signal is positive, TR1 is switched on and it pulls the control voltage to IC1 much lower than its normal level. This produces a greatly reduced output frequency. The actual output frequencies are approximately 40kHz and 60kHz.

The receiver circuit is shown in Figures 3.25 and 3.26. The circuit for the detector, amplifier, and monostable stages

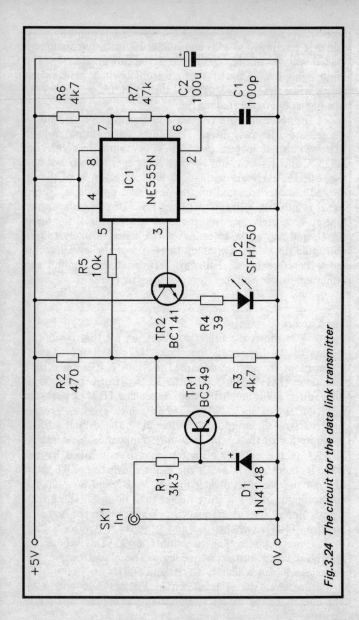

Fig.3.24 *The circuit for the data link transmitter*

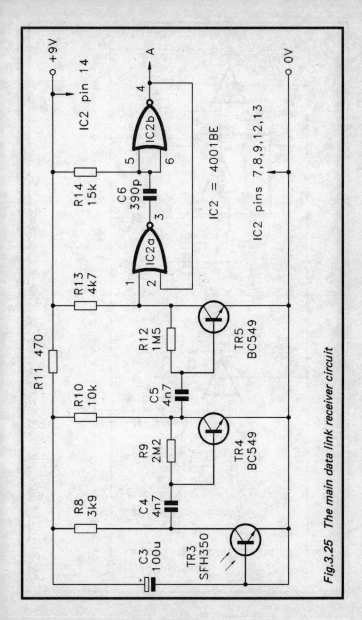

Fig.3.25 The main data link receiver circuit

133

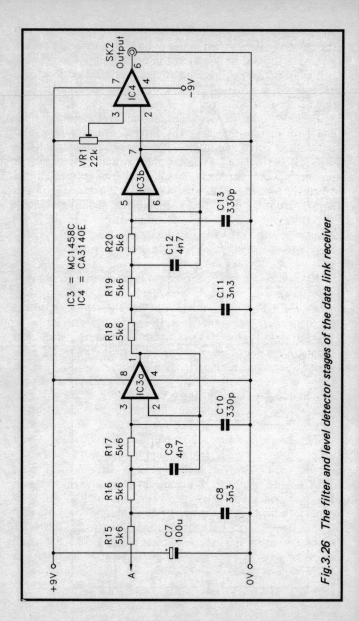

Fig.3.26 The filter and level detector stages of the data link receiver

134

are shown in Figure 3.25. This section of the circuit is much the same as its equivalent in the audio link described previously, and it will not be considered in detail here. The detector is a phototransistor, but the circuit will also work using a photodiode provided the value of R8 is increased to 15k (see Figure 3.20).

Figure 3.26 shows the circuit diagram for the lowpass filter and level detector stages. The filter consists of two third order filters connected in series, giving a total attenuation rate of 36dB per octave. The maximum switching frequency is produced when the input signal is alternate "marks" and "spaces", and with a 19200 baud signal is 9.6kHz. The filter's cutoff frequency is at about double this figure, enabling a 19200 baud signal to be easily accommodated. The filter gives about 40dB of attenuation at the lower carrier frequency, so there is a reasonably low ripple content on the output from IC3b.

IC4 is an operational amplifier which is used here as a voltage comparator. VR1 is connected as a potential divider across the supply rails, and it provides the reference voltage to the non-inverting input of IC4. In order to drive an RS232C input properly IC4 must be operated with dual supplies. In practice, and provided a short connecting cable is used between SK2 and the RS232C port, it may well be found that the circuit will drive most RS232C inputs with pin 4 of IC4 simply wired to the 0 volt supply rail. However, in order to be certain that the circuit will drive any RS232C input properly it is essential to use a negative supply for IC4.

The circuit of Figure 3.27 can be used to produce a −9 volt supply from the main +9 volt supply, and this is often the most convenient way of handling things. This circuit utilizes an ICL7660, which is a switching device specifically designed for an application of this type. Note that the ICL7660 has a maximum input voltage rating of 10 volts, and that a nominal 9 volt supply is the highest that should be used. The loaded output voltage will be somewhat less than −9 volts, but it will be more than adequate to ensure that IC4 can drive an RS232C input reliability.

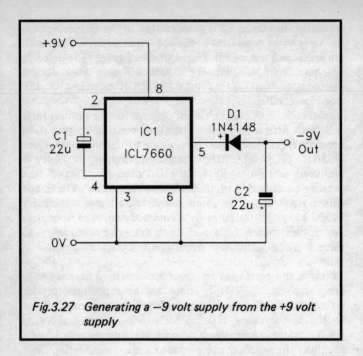

Fig.3.27 Generating a —9 volt supply from the +9 volt supply

Adjustment

25 way D connectors have been specified for the input and output sockets, as these are the standard connectors for RS232C ports. However, as in this case only two connecting wires are used, it would be reasonable to opt for a simple two way connector such as a jack type. As described here the unit only provides simplex (one way) operation with no handshaking. For duplex (two way) operation it is necessary to use two systems and two fibre-optic cables, with a separate system carrying the RS232C signal in each direction. If handshaking is required, probably the easiest method is to build a two way system and select software (XON—XOFF) handshaking. It should be possible to use further fibre-optic links in order to implement hardware handshaking, but I have not tried this. Where possible it is best to use a baud rate that transfers the data at a rate that the receiving device can cope

with. Handshaking is then unnecessary.

The system was found to work well using a fibre-optic cable 20 metres long. It should work over somewhat greater distances, but I have not tried it using a longer cable. Unlike a system that uses an ordinary (wire) connecting cable, the maximum usable baud rate is largely independent of the cable length.

If suitable test gear is available, couple a 10kHz squarewave signal at a few volts peak to peak to the input of the transmitter. Use an oscilloscope to monitor the output from the receiver, and adjust VR1 for a 1 to 1 mark-space ratio. It is possible to set VR1 correctly without the aid of suitable test equipment. The computer connected to the transmitter should be set up to repeatedly send a short group of characters at the highest baud rate that the system will need to handle. The receiving system should be set up so that it prints received characters onto the screen of the monitor. There should be a narrow range of settings which provide uncorrupted data on the screen of the receiving terminal. VR1 is adjusted to the middle of this range of settings.

Components for Fibre-Optic Data Link – Transmitter (Fig.3.24)

Resistors (all 0.25 watt 5% carbon film)

R1	3k3
R2	470R
R3	4k7
R4	39R
R5	10k
R6	4k7
R7	47k

Capacitors

C1	100p polystyrene
C2	100μ 10V elect

Semiconductors

IC1	NE555N
TR1	BC549

TR2	BC141
D1	1N4148
D2	SFH750 or similar

Miscellaneous

SK1	25 way D connector
	Case
	Circuit board
	8 pin DIL IC holder
	Wire, solder, etc.

Components for Fibre-Optic Data Link – Receiver (Figs 3.25 & 3.26)

Resistors (all 0.25 watt 5% carbon film)

R8	3k9 (see text)
R9	2M2
R10	10k
R11	470R
R12	1M5
R13	4k7
R14	15k
R15 to R20	5k6 (6 off)

Potentiometer

| VR1 | 22k min preset |

Capacitors

C3	100µ 10V elect
C4	4n7 polyester
C5	4n7 polyester
C6	390p polystyrene
C7	100µ 10V elect
C8	3n3 polyester
C9	4n7 polyester
C10	330p polystyrene
C11	3n3 polyester
C12	4n7 polyester
C13	330p polystyrene

Semiconductors

TR3	SFH350 (see text)
TR4	BC549
TR5	BC549
IC2	4001BE
IC3	MC1458C
IC4	CA3140E

Miscellaneous

SK2	25 way D connector
	Case
	Circuit board
	8 pin DIL IC holder (2 off)
	14 pin DIL IC holder
	Standard 2.2/1mm fibre-optic cable
	Wire, solder, etc.

Components for −9 Volt Supply Generator (Fig.3.27)

Capacitors

C1	22μ 16V elect
C2	22μ 16V elect

Semiconductors

IC1	ICL7660
D1	1N4148
	8 pin DIL IC holder

Notes